PRAISE
AT GOD'S HOUSE

"This book is a must-read for those of us who feel and think and grind through the days knowing that with courage there can be peace. Even just for a minute. *Dinner at God's House* is not just Lieman's story. It belongs to all of us. A beautiful and raw story about healing and the choice to live in courage or fear."

— **Lara Love Hardin, author of *The Many Lives of Mama Love***
and six-time *New York Times* bestselling author

"I was reminded of Richard Bach's books as I read *Dinner at God's House*. Lieman writes in raw, emotional prose that makes you want to turn the pages quickly as you are carried through each vivid scene. A must-read for those seeking inspiration and fuel for their own spiritual journey."

— **Jacob Nordby, author of**
Blessed Are the Weird* and *The Creative Cure

"*Dinner at God's House* is what happens when you are ready to get really, truly honest, which is the biggest adventure of all. This brave, engaging, heartfelt book is a gift."

— **Nanea Hoffman, author**
and founder of Sweatpants & Coffee

"Nick Hornby meets *The Alchemist*. Lieman has touched on something in this book that few authors can—handling the greatest mysteries of life, the heartbreaks and disappointments with so much grace and honesty."

—**Anna-Marie O'Brien, author of**
Adventures of a Metalhead Librarian

DiNNER AT GOD'S HOUSE

DINNER AT GOD'S HOUSE

Todd B. Lieman

Wellness Writers Press

WELLNESS WRITERS PRESS
An imprint of Pure Ink Press

Paperback ISBN: 979-8-9894541-0-5
Ebook ISBN: 979-8-9894541-1-2

Library of Congress Control Number: 2024900146

Cover design by Daniel Robert Cohn (namastepictures.com)
Concept and creative direction by Paul Norwood (paulnorwood.com)

wellnesswriterspress.com
www.pureinkpress.com

Look to this day
for it is life
the very life of life.
In its brief course lie all
the realities and truths of existence:
the joy of growth
the splendor of action
the glory of power.
For yesterday is but a memory
and tomorrow is only a vision.
But today well lived
makes every yesterday a memory of happiness
and every tomorrow a vision of hope.
Look well, therefore, to this day.
-Kālidāsa-

For Lisa & Kolby . . .
and for family, friends,
and all who seek the miracle of a day well lived

"I do believe in an everyday sort of magic—the inexplicable connectedness we sometimes experience with places, people, works of art and the like; the eerie appropriateness of moments of synchronicity; the whispered voice, the hidden presence, when we think we're alone."

—CHARLES DE LINT

PROLOGUE

There are loud voices and an endless, monotonous beeping outside my window. As I look down from my blank, white-walled second-floor office onto the street scene just below, I see an elderly woman being placed on a stretcher and loaded into the back of an ambulance. I stare at a blinking cursor and know exactly why I'm seeing this scene: the Universe has a way of providing perspective when you need it most.

"Trust yourself." They were my bigger-than-life editor's last words to me before handing over this project.

I know they were meant to inspire me and, more importantly, give me permission to share the truth. To write from my soul. They were meant to give me consent to go to that place—that deep, deep place that can only be found under the glowing light of faith. Of loving myself. The place I've long struggled to find. My editor was telling me to believe in myself.

Easier said than done.

I've spent hours staring at that damn cursor. I want to please this editor of mine. Not because I'm desperate for approval, but because telling this story comes with massive responsibility. It's a hard story to believe, I know. But it's important for me to tell it. Imperative. Imposter syndrome is perhaps greatest when the words are at their most significant.

Sometimes, it's easier to live in fear than it is to live in the raw transparency of authenticity. Fear is an excuse. Authenticity is an

1

ultimatum: take it or leave it. Take me or leave me. No excuses available if "leave me" is the choice others take. It's a risk to trust yourself enough and love yourself enough to choose authenticity. It's brave. Authenticity shouldn't have to be brave. It should be the norm. Not a special menu item, but the usual.

It's not.

I wonder if the woman on the stretcher is contemplating the narrative of her life. Is she satisfied with the choices she made? Is she feeling regret? Can she surrender to whatever she's experiencing, or is she fighting with questions? Is she wondering, *why me?* Seeing the ambulance pull away from the curb with its flashing lights and wailing siren makes me consider the urgency of this moment.

I feel tremendous pressure to get these words right. I suppose every writer does. These words, as with any, have the potential to cause others great harm. I've already ignorantly done enough of that in my life, so I certainly do not want to willfully do it now.

But what if I told you that God told me to write this book? That God is the editor I mentioned. Even if your God is not my God. What if your God told you to write a book? I'm not even sure I understand it. Maybe now you understand my pressure.

I'll do the best I can.

Welcome to my attempt to trust myself.

Much Love,
Erik

CHAPTER ONE

Don't look down.

Don't look down.

Please, please, just don't look down!

Pinned against the majestic red and orange face of the sheer rock wall—which, despite being only fifty feet or so above the ground, seemed to reach millions of feet into the sky—I begged myself not to look down! My heart pounded and echoed violently throughout my body. My pulse boomed like the 808s blasting from the blackened windows of a slow-moving, lowered muscle car. With my arms and legs spread wide and my body pinned flat against the wall, I desperately gripped the smallest of natural shelves.

Just hold on, I prayed.

Don't let go, I begged.

Only the toes of my new knobby hiking boots—the ones with the Vibram soles, the ones I just had to have—were connected to Mother Nature. *Why did I need these big-ass boots?* I wanted to throw up. *Breathe.*

I think I was fourteen at the time. No, twelve . . . Eleven. I was eleven. Come to think of it, could I have been younger? Doesn't matter. What matters is, that was the first time I remember consciously thinking about my death. I had experienced death with my goldfish and my dog, but on that rock was the first time I had ever considered my own.

Who would come to my funeral?

That's how eleven-year-olds process thoughts like death. As if there were some right answer that would make it all okay. *As long as* he's *there, I'm cool with letting go of this rock.*

I was in Joshua Tree National Park with my scout troop. I had wandered away from the others to climb on some of the world's most famous rock formations. I wasn't much of a daredevil and certainly wasn't a skilled climber, so I played it safe. *I always played it safe.* That was exactly why I was all alone and my predicament was particularly ironic.

My fellow scouts, who neither realized nor cared that I only joined their troop because my parents thought it might be a good idea, were fearless. And, because I didn't want to face the inevitable hazing that always came with declining whatever stupid thing they wanted to do, I got proactive.

"I want to check out that rock over there," I told them, pointing to the beautiful yet harmless formation that was more *Brontosaurus* than *T-rex*. "Who wants to come with me?" I invited them, knowing full well that nobody would want to join.

They looked. They laughed. Not enough danger. My rock ate plants. They were carnivores and had something else planned. Something that couldn't possibly end well. The bloody race to the ER had happened enough times before that I knew I wanted no part of it. Like the time they tried climbing a redwood tree. *A redwood!* I'd watched from a safe distance as Billy Stevens lost his grip a few feet from the ground, fell awkwardly, and broke his arm. Keith McDonald ended up with a concussion.

Undaunted, it only strengthened their resolve to continue the quest to prove Darwin's theory of evolution. They thought I was weak. My scoutmaster didn't exactly help. He once hiked six miles on a broken leg. "I'm fine," he'd told us. Even at eleven, I thought that was fucking idiotic. The others thought his mangled bone was legendary.

They declined my invitation and mumbled something about a faraway crevasse. They wanted to climb to crazy heights *and then* jump across some silly crack high in the sky. Back and forth. Over and over. Slip, and they wouldn't just break a leg or end up concussed.

4

They'd die. *Fun!* No way I was doing that. No chance at all. I quietly made a bet with myself about the number of guys who would get hurt and the total number of stitches they might collectively need. *Smart money is on Keith. Smart money was always on Keith. Over-under on the stitches: 150.*

With a couple of hours left before sunset, they scampered off in a chorus of hoots and hollers. I tried to ignore the insults they threw at me under their breaths. *Loser. Why is he always such a pussy? Our troop would be so much better without his lame ass.* I heard them all as I made my way to my gentle herbivore in the exact opposite direction. I didn't look back as I walked away, convinced that I didn't care. A single tear suggested otherwise.

If I had been able to understand myself back then, I'd have seen that my fears and that tear were rooted in self-consciousness. I was shorter than most of my classmates. Not by much, but just enough to notice. And while I wasn't exactly fat, I wasn't fit. I remember sitting on a desk wearing shorts, and my thighs flattened out like two big life rafts. A girl walked by and laughed.

My haircut wasn't bad, but . . .

I wasn't the dumbest, but . . .

That's just kind of how it went for me. I was the other half of the sentence. The half that always told me I wasn't quite enough.

My boulder wasn't giant. Navigating it was less like climbing and more like hiking. It was that easy. That forgiving. The footholds were as big as kitchen tables. I didn't even need my hands as I scrambled toward the low clouds.

At what was essentially only a few feet off the ground, the view was, I don't know, kind of hard for an eleven-year-old to describe. I hadn't yet learned the words that could truly capture how I felt in that moment. I didn't know too many words that could describe how I felt back then. I didn't know I was allowed to feel.

Just a few feet up, I could see giant, granite dinosaurs guarding the hallowed Joshua Tree grounds. They took on mystical forms that seemed to vibrate and glow. They were alive and painted with a majestic palette of time. The monsters were surrounded by beautiful prickly cacti. *I suppose that's how many people are too.* The rocks guarded the grounds; the cacti guarded the rocks. A perfectly symbiotic relationship. The desert's version of sharks and remora fish.

Because that was before mobile phones, I couldn't take pictures or share anything on an Instagram story. I could only experience the moment as it was. The images burned into my brain. I sat in silence and felt a sense of accomplishment. I loved being alone. I wouldn't have appreciated it all if the others had been there. They wouldn't have allowed for that. They would have been making jokes, daring each other to jump, or throwing rocks. They wouldn't have cared about the colors or the textures. They wouldn't have noticed the sun reflecting off the clouds or heard the sound of desert silence. They wouldn't have been aware enough to discover that cool air has taste. Like ice gripping your tongue. The fact that I was able to acknowledge those experiences added to my outcast status.

I didn't belong with them. I didn't belong anywhere.

They were all in the distance, beyond the Joshua trees, dinosaurs, and succulents. I thought about calling out but didn't want to stir the silence. I didn't know it was the Universe, per se, that I was hesitant to disturb; it just didn't feel right to yell. I waved, but they simply carried on. Completely oblivious to the magic and the spirit that surrounded all of us.

I wasn't. Even if I didn't understand it. I felt insignificant, and I liked it. My young energy felt meaningless among the ancient desert spirits. Peaceful. At that moment, I didn't care what anybody thought of me. I didn't have to try to fit in. *You guys go do whatever you want to do. I couldn't possibly be happier right now.*

I wish I had learned to pay more attention to that feeling. I was too young to interpret its significance and power. I might have unconsciously ignored it because acknowledging it made me feel different. And being different scared me. I was taught to fit in at all costs. Being myself and thinking for myself were not really on the table. Instead, I learned to lie to make others feel better. I learned to suppress my happiness if I thought it might make others feel bad. I lied to protect others. I lied to protect myself. And even though the lies made me feel worse, the more I lied, the more I was accepted.

That boulder, like most rock formations in Joshua Tree, was part of a bigger structure. Emboldened by the elixir of accomplishment and inner peace, I started up a more difficult, but still completely manageable, climb. I needed to use my hands and take my time with the ascent. Loose rocks slipped away under my feet as I nearly lost my footing more than once.

Did I just alter history?

How long have those small rocks been there?

Did the rocks know they were there?

Did they know each other?

Were they friends?

Did I just break up a family?

I felt bad for the rocks. I really did. That's how my brain worked. That's how my heart worked. I had always felt things that others didn't. I felt everything. Even the pain a rock might feel. I closed my eyes and apologized to Mother Nature. Another prayer. I wasn't paying attention as I kept moving and climbing.

Without any warning, I found myself higher than I had ever been. Higher than I had intended to go. As I attempted to take another step, I realized I was stuck. High above the desert floor, I couldn't move. I was pinned flat against the sheer rock wall. I had no idea what to do. My throat was dry. My cries for help were silent.

Who would come to my funeral?

I tried not to look down. But I had to. What other choice did I have? Of course, I was going to look down. *Wait!* I noticed a boy about my age looking up at me. He was wearing a white T-shirt and jeans. A red baseball cap was turned backward on his head. I tried to figure out what kind of hat it was to distract myself.

That must be an Angels hat.

Their spring training facility isn't too far from here.

I wonder who the Angels are playing today.

I sure hope Don Baylor has a great season.

Rod Carew is awesome, but Bobby Grich is my favorite player.

That went on for what felt like hours. It was probably closer to thirty seconds. I needed to ask for help, but I was afraid that yelling would cause me to lose my grip. The boy was looking up at me. At least, I thought he was. I hoped he would notice I was in trouble based on my spread-eagle pose on the side of the wall.

Please, I prayed. *Go get help.*

The boy ran off with urgency. I was certain I was about to be saved. I had a moment when I thought of him asking my fellow scouts to rescue me and felt like I'd rather just die. At least I'd still have my dignity. Then I considered that I might be high enough off the ground to earn their respect.

When he didn't come back, and with the sun setting, I again began to wonder who would come to my funeral. I wondered if anyone would cry. I wondered if my fellow scouts would make fun of me. *Oh, stop.* They weren't going to be there and certainly weren't coming to rescue me.

I wasn't ready to die. I didn't want to give the others that satisfaction. I promised myself I'd get off the rock alive.

Which was exactly what I did.

As much as I'd like to describe the brave and treacherous descent, as much as I'd like to remember how I got down, I think I blacked out and was rescued by my fear. One second, I was on the rock, and the next, I was on the ground—with no recollection of climbing down.

Confused, I found my way back to my troop on wobbly legs. I kept looking back at the rock, hoping I'd recognize some path down. A line. There wasn't one.

How did I get off the rock?

Did I actually climb down?

Did I float down?

Was I carried?

Am I going crazy?

I had zero understanding of how I got from there to here. I asked the rock what happened. It didn't answer. I thanked it for saving me anyway. For years, I would tell this story to blank stares and obvious thought bubbles filled with comments like, "Wow, Erik, you smoked crack when you were eleven?" I finally stopped telling the story when one of my therapists suggested it meant I belonged on meds. I told him to fuck off. I may very well have belonged on meds, but not for that.

While it's most logical to think I blacked out to overcome the fear, I've come to grips with a different truth. I didn't climb down. I was lifted by some other force. Some other energy. I was so connected to the frequency of the Universe that I became one with that energy. I *was* that energy. I left my body, floated down, and reunited with the physical shell of myself. I'd always wanted it to happen again. It was a life event that defined the kind of spiritual partnership I wanted with the Universe. I wish I could have run with that moment and let that experience become the guiding light of my life. I didn't. I couldn't.

I never felt confident or comfortable enough to deal with being on the outside looking in. I needed to fit in. Even when it came at the expense of my personal truth—or any truth for that matter. So I lied. Over and over and over and over. And I was rewarded for those lies. With acceptance. Laughter. Sex. That's how I was programmed. My truth felt unacceptable. When I would try it on and wade into the shallow end of spirituality with my friends, they'd just laugh. Fear preyed on my fight-or-flight response. It knew I would never fight. So, flight it was.

I didn't know what authenticity meant when I was eleven. Nobody talked like that all those years ago. It wasn't a thing. But it was what I most wanted. To be understood and seen and accepted for being nothing but myself. It took nearly five decades to discover that what I truly wanted was the ability to love and accept myself. I was looking for others to do that for me. If I could have loved myself, it wouldn't have mattered who did or didn't love me. Or who did or didn't accept me. Instead, I just pushed everyone away. Including the person in the mirror.

Especially the person in the mirror.

Loving myself seemed so simple yet always felt impossible. It may very well be at the top of the "Things I Know Yet Cannot Find Any Way to Do Anything About" list. It's a *long* list.

While sitting around the campfire that night with my fellow scouts, I forced myself to pretend nothing extraordinary had happened. I did what I did best: I lied. I told them about the rock I sat on. I told them I could see them all in the distance, and that I had waved. I made the rock significantly lower and lied about the descent. They were going to laugh at me anyway. They told me I was lame. My scout leader laughed at me, too, as he applied bandages to Keith's badly-wounded knee. I thought his injuries would be worse; I felt bad for wishing they were.

In a moment of weakness, I asked them if they saw the kid with the backward baseball hat.

"There's nobody else near us," they told me. "What are you talking about? Now he's seeing things. What a d-bag." More high fives. More laughs from the scout leader.

From that day on the wall in Joshua Tree, death became something that was never far from my thoughts or my experiences. I thought about it pretty much every day. Multiple times a day. Needless to say, death was front of mind as I sat in the back corner of the synagogue, watching my own funeral.

CHAPTER TWO

Adopted at birth, a professional football coach sets out to find his birth parents. His dad, who never knew he had a son, turns out to be the coach's mentor of nearly three decades.[1]

I never cared much for organized religion. Still, the rituals, traditions, and community remained intriguing. Raised best described as a cultural Jew, I liked the way I felt in a synagogue or gathered around a Passover table. I liked the way cultural rituals like the *seder* plate or searching for a broken piece of *matzoh* brought family, friends, and strangers together. It created a safer space to think about what a friend's young son once described as "life's bigger questions."

I just never liked the idea that I was supposed to believe in only one thing or another. I didn't have the kind of belief that some sky spirit could be all knowing. And I really didn't subscribe to the idea that all things could be explained away by "God's plan."

I did the Bar Mitzvah thing, collected my money, and gave a speech about being afraid of nuclear war. Both before and after that, I felt a connection to something. It felt like an energy, which would much later be defined for me as the Universe. I liked that. I liked thinking about the Universe as energy without having to drift into religion or defend my feelings and uncertainty about God. But I remained uncomfortable talking about it for fear of being labeled a New-Age weirdo. Sharing my spiritual thoughts and desires made me feel like an outcast around

11

my friends, family, and, well, just about anyone. In my world, you were either religious or you weren't. Anything in between was freaky. And "spiritual"? *Ugh.*

Privately, I felt like I *was part* of something bigger. Like I was a kind of connective tissue. A root system. A messenger. I was taught to believe that faith and religion were conjoined twins. I didn't think I was allowed to have faith without religion. As I grew older, I'd roll my eyes at people who called themselves spiritual healers; and yet, it was what I think I wanted most to be. It was how I felt about myself. Instead, I lied to myself and built a career as far from that as possible. I was surrounded by testosterone and bravado, devoid of authenticity—and found myself in rooms filled with men named "Bro."

On my own, I sat in on different services. Buddhist. Baptist. Episcopalian. I didn't always believe what the others in the room believed, but I felt like I could hide in my little corner and pray the way I needed to pray. It was more meditative than religious. It was spiritual. Reflective. It was faith. My faith.

I liked Temple Beth Am. It was different. There was no stained glass. There was no *bima* upon which the services were performed. It wasn't even a real synagogue. Temple Beth Am was an empty, open ground floor in a nondescript, white office building that the congregation rented for services. When you walked through the building lobby and into the temporary synagogue, smiling members of the youth group distributed well-worn, hand-me-down prayer books. So many pages bent or torn. Some covers even ripped. It didn't matter. Temple Beth Am was also missing the most prevalent trait found in all of my previous Jewish experiences: guilt. It had no history of "that's not how we've always done it." The place felt raw and rough around the edges because it was. A blue-collar kind of Jewish ethic for its white-collar congregants. Culture over religion. I could be invisible and anonymous there. I could be spiritual and accepted there. Nobody cared.

Temple Beth Am was the anti-synagogue. I felt as much at home there as I ever had in such a place. I felt it immediately when, sometime in my early forties, I opened the generic glass door for the first time.

When I found it, I thought that was where I would finally let go of a past that haunted me. I didn't believe I could pray away my mistakes, but I did believe I could find peace within myself. For myself. There, I could accept and celebrate that I floated off a rock at Joshua Tree. I could forgive myself for the pain I caused others. I could forgive myself for the pain I caused myself. I could talk to my God without judgment. Even with no clue as to what God meant to me. Even as others in the room may have been completely clear on what God meant to them. Their God didn't have to be my God.

My funeral was about to start when I settled into a back corner as far removed as possible from the ceremony that would take place in front. It was where I always sat. As if I were creating a safe distance from any religious formality that might possibly occur in the orchestra seats. Like avoiding the front row at SeaWorld. Even in a place as chill as Temple Beth Am, I didn't want any religion to splash on me. As the light outside poured through the double-pane office windows, I felt cold.

The room was packed with mourners representing stages of my life—even Keith and Billy, who were with me in Joshua Tree decades earlier. They were the two scouts I kept in touch with. I was always good at that. Holding onto friends and relationships. Even the ones I should have let go of. Goddamn, I sucked at letting go. Keith had scratches on his face, and his arm was in a sling—the result of a mountain biking accident I read about on Facebook.

Almost everyone was kind enough to dispense with the traditional formalities of black suits, black dresses, black whatever. I wasn't much for black clothes, and these people, my people, filled the room with color. My parents sat in the front row with their respective significant others. They had divorced shortly after my not-quite-near-death experience. I was only eleven, yet I was old enough to know they had no business being together. I didn't know what happened behind the closed doors of moms and dads. But at eleven, I felt like I knew how love should look and sound. And I knew it didn't sound or look anything like my parents.

My mom, dressed in black from head to toe, cried as my sister started to speak. Six years older than me, my sister told stories that masked her insecurities and regrets by giving the impression of a closeness we never had. There was the story about helping me with my homework when I was a freshman in high school and she was in college. Yes, I had called for help, but it never came. I didn't really need the help; I was just trying to find a way to connect with her. I always desperately wanted to connect with her.

Then she told the story of my first kiss. I was twelve, and she knew I had a big crush on her friend, who, in my young mind, was a perfect goddess. Helen was the reason I loved brunettes. She was an otherworldly high school senior who ran track and drove a black Mazda RX-7 with a license plate frame that said "CATCH ME" on top and "IF YOU CAN" on the bottom. I could barely speak anytime Helen came home with my sister.

One time, as the story goes, Helen knocked on the front door when my sister wasn't home. I mumbled something about nothing, and she said she would wait in my sister's room. I went back into mine. After a few minutes, she knocked on my bedroom door. She started asking questions about my soccer team and the teachers I had. I managed to answer, and she moved onto my bed where I was working. And she kissed me. Just like that. As she walked out, she said, "You're a great kid. If only you were a little older."

As my sister told this story at my funeral, I was hearing for the first time that she had set up the whole thing. She and Helen conspired to bring me a second of joy that lasted a lifetime. I had no idea. Everyone in the room laughed. But seriously, had I known, I would have given my sister my allowance for life. I would have done the dishes forever. I would have been nicer to her. I guess it wasn't really our fault—at six years apart, we were more like two only children growing up in the same house. We were barely part of the same generation, and it wasn't like our parents modeled healthy love and respect. But she tried, and I missed it. I fucking missed it.

Damn. What else did I miss?

My sister walked back to her seat, and my mom sobbed. My dad looked at her, rolled his eyes, and whispered something to his current wife. She shushed him. I knew it was a sarcastic, inappropriate comment. He did that when he was uncomfortable. My parents had been divorced for longer than they had been married, but nothing had changed. At least they didn't fight anymore.

After the prayers, a song or two, and a few nice words from the rabbi, Dr. Timmy was the last to speak. That's exactly how I wanted it. I appreciated that my parents figured that out. Tall, chiseled, and always with what I called his "nine o'clock shadow" because five o'clock was just too early for Timmy, he would have been a cliché from HotSurgeons.com.

Timmy was my longest-tenured best friend. There were others, like Larry and Greg from childhood and Adam and Dan more recently, but Timmy had been around the longest and was the most consistent. He never took it for granted. Neither of us did. He was best friend emeritus. We lived together in college. We lived together after college. And in the thirty-plus years we had known each other, we never, ever, *ever* lost touch. That's what separated him from all others. If anyone knew, *truly* knew, where all the bodies were buried, no pun intended, it was Timmy. He should speak last. I was glad he spoke last.

Timmy normally wore designer jeans and a designer T-shirt to perfectly compliment his designer shave, and this day was no different. Despite the setting, his shirt, except for the front as fashion dictated, remained untucked. From my invisible spot situated in the back of the synagogue, I approved. I would have been especially disappointed if Timmy had worn a suit.

As I looked around the room, I felt sad. Maybe that was the cold I was feeling. Maybe in death, feelings become temperature. I don't know. I started feeling like I was going to miss these people. I was going to miss Timmy. Still, I wondered which of the women seated in the temple Timmy would fuck. He got laid at every wedding we ever attended together—even my ill-conceived, quickly-annulled mistake when I was in my early twenties.

Ever the romantic, I forever wanted to marry someone I had just met. So I did. Only it wasn't such a good idea. Stacy and I turned out to have nothing in common beyond an insatiable desire to fuck. Anywhere and everywhere. But when the heat wore off, we were a disaster. Wasn't her fault. Wasn't my fault. Timmy got laid at that impromptu wedding under a table, I think. Seemed kind of beautiful to get laid at my funeral. He'd do it with grace. It was his gift. I'd bet on Leslie. They always had a connection and were always teasing each other. This was the perfect opportunity to consummate the perfect friends-with-benefits relationship. One last chance to be Timmy's wingman, I smiled at Leslie. I was going to miss being Timmy's wingman.

He spoke. "The nickname by which you knew Erik Bernstein immediately told the story of when and how you met him. If you called him Skippy, you knew him as a little kid who started skipping before he walked. If you knew Skipper, you went to college together, where he developed a reputation for skipping more classes than he attended. That gave way to Link in honor of all the time he spent playing Nintendo games and then Berns, Bernie, Bernsie, and Bernstein throughout his career. I called him Shirl."

It's true. I loved nicknames. Each one a perfectly conceived shield. A wall. An NFL-sized defensive lineman who kept most people one step further away from knowing me. *But I called him by a nickname! We're buddies!* They were a purposeful, false intimacy. Because if you call someone by a nickname, you can be fooled into thinking you're that much closer.

"He didn't let many in. Not all the way. But Erik always gave you just enough to feel special. All these nicknames made sure of that. Today, though, we take away the nicknames and we reveal the man. Today, we honor . . . Erik."

Jesus Christ, Timmy. Fuck me. *What's with all this intimacy? Where the fuck is that coming from?* I rarely let people know me and often felt like my loneliest and safest place on the planet was a room packed full of people who were supposed to be friends. An intuitive once told me that I lived life on the outside looking in, more an observer than a participant. She said I lived a life filled with fear. As a result, I talked a much bigger game than I lived.

She was right. I had a closet full of masks that hid my true self—my true identity. They removed any chance that I might get hurt. They also removed any chance that I might be loved. They helped me avoid by creating a void. There's that old "if I only knew then what I know now" cliché. Well, fuck. It's never truer than after you die. John Lennon sang of instant karma. As Timmy spoke, I experienced instant regret.

He continued. "Erik loved the movie *Cocktail*. God only knows why. He must have watched it a hundred times during the years we lived together. There's a scene in the movie when Bryan Brown's character bets that Tom Cruise's character has some kind of business book under the bar. Erik was that way with books about the human spirit. He read them constantly."

Timmy took a moment to choke back some tears as his voice cracked uncharacteristically.

"My God, how he loved people. He loved their ability to overcome, to be torn down, and to rise again. He loved their ability to create. He loved vulnerability. He loved when they 'put themselves out there,' as he'd say. He marveled at the singer-songwriter playing to an empty bar, yet still performing as though he were in front of a packed house at Carnegie Hall. He read those books because he wanted to be one of those people. He wanted to move people. He wanted to inspire them. And he did. Even if he could never accept it. He wanted to be one of those people. And he was. Even if he couldn't see it."

I looked around and saw heads nodding. My friends dabbed their eyes with the sleeves of their shirts. This was kind of how I imagined it when I was on that wall in Joshua Tree. Except everyone was older now.

Tim was still talking. "He always said he wanted to know what it felt like to be whole. To belong. Because he never really felt like he did. He was always searching. Always wanting to ask bigger questions. So he had these books hidden around his house the way an alcoholic hides his booze. He didn't want anyone to know. Frankly, I thought this search he was on was kind of ridiculous. As a dyed-in-the-wool-no-apologies atheist, I'm a science addict. Erik would try to talk to me about this universal energy shit, and I just couldn't help but roll my eyes. He made me insane with 'the Universe this' and 'the Universe that.'"

I had tortured him with my talk of the Universe. He tolerated it. I remember sitting on the worn-out leather stools at The Gym, each of us nursing our brown drinks and half-assedly watching a game on the TV above the bar when I asked him if he ever thought about death. "What the fuck kind of question is that?" he asked. "Is this one of your universal energy quizzes?"

"Never mind," I told him. "Just kidding." I got up from my seat, put a bar napkin on top of my glass, and told him I was going to go outside to watch the cars.

I loved watching cars from an early age. I always said you could learn much about a community at a four-way stop. It was like a social experiment. Cars told stories of affluence. Of influence. Of leaders and followers. The number of rolling stops gives away privilege. The full-blown "fuck you" of the Mercedes SUV driver who doesn't even bother to wait his rightful turn screams entitlement. The number of Teslas told of trends and rich former hippies. And the number of really beat-up cars that were clearly uninsured told a story of hired help.

I called it "the dance." If you spend enough time watching the choreography of who goes when or who waves to whom, you begin to develop an ability to predict the general behaviors of, well, anyone. I could walk around town, point to a car, and tell you the story of the driver. Intersections are undervalued social experiments.

Because of the way the street was marked, as many as nine cars could be stopped simultaneously at the four-way intersection outside The Gym. And when all nine cars were there, I was in my happy place. I loved to watch the confusion unfold. Sure, there were laws that dictated what was supposed to happen when, but I was more intrigued by the psychology that seemed to preempt those laws. There are good people. And there are assholes. I figured if they balanced each other in total numbers, we were going to be okay. Every time I watched, I just needed one person to wave someone ahead, and it would make my day better. Like one good golf shot can save an entire shitty round.

Timmy cleared his throat and continued speaking. "Erik loved watching cars. Always pointing out some impatient asshole who believed that his time was more important than the others and, therefore, he shouldn't have to wait his turn. This guy, Erik would suggest, was so full of himself that he thought it was a bother to even pretend to stop. This driver's actions were met with the usual orchestra of horns, rage, and middle-finger gestures from the other drivers. Especially, as Erik said, from the Lululemon-wearing housewives on their way to yoga, Pilates, tennis, therapy, the pharmacy, getting laid, picking up the kids, or going to soccer practice."

I laughed. Some of my friends used to describe taking a shit as "dropping off the kids." And I knew a few women who referred to getting their recreational prescription drugs as "picking up the kids."

Tim proceeded. "Erik once told me that he imagined that the Mercedes driver would soon be home to his unhappy household. As a result of running the stop sign, our driver would arrive home just a few minutes earlier than expected and find his wife twisted into a most unfortunate position by the young neighbor boy, recently home from college and full of unlimited stamina. If he had only waited his turn, his wife's lover might have escaped, and nobody would be the wiser. Instead, that rolling stop cost Mercedes Guy half his net worth. Erik loved that."

I didn't really. I pretended I did. I even lied to my closest, best, most intimate friends. I needed to fake it. I needed a mask. Even with them. Mostly, I just hated the way Mercedes Guy treated other people. I didn't want his life destroyed. The truth is that he was probably unhappy for a huge number of reasons that neither Tim nor I would ever understand. I sucked for making jokes about him. I sucked for pretending to root against his family. I sucked for acting like I thought it was funny that he was miserable. But that's what I did. Always.

My reactions to this guy were counter to the way I had wanted to live. Counter to the guy I wanted to be. When I said shit like that and got laughs, I felt horrible. But just like my dad, sarcasm carried me through the times I felt uncomfortable. For the first time ever, I looked at my dad and wondered what he was hiding. I wondered what my dad's authentic self looked and sounded like. I cannot believe I hadn't thought of that before. Damn. *Sorry, Dad. I should have noticed. I should have asked.*

"Ironically, Erik died in this intersection. I imagine him having total consciousness for that brief second, knowing it was his time and experiencing something he had never known: peace. The very thing he had strived to find in the pages of his books. I like to imagine that he felt it. Even just for that second."

Timmy wiped another tear away from his eyes and looked at Jess. Not even I could look at Jess. "One of his favorite teachers died golfing. Erik always said he thought it was the most beautiful, poetic death imaginable. No pain. Doing what he loved. Erik always said we should all die in our happy place. As fate would have it, so it went for Erik."

Timmy was using fate generally, like all of us had at one time or another, but the fact is, fate had absolutely nothing to do with it.

CHAPTER THREE

*While preparing for their wedding, a young couple finds a picture
of themselves both playing on the same beach just a few feet apart
from one another—eleven years before they met and fell in love.*[2]

My friends congregated at The Gym. As it should be. I sat on the far
southeast corner of my intersection and watched them arrive one by
one—each skillfully navigating their way through "the dance." I was
proud as I watched them all do the right thing. Taking their proper
turns and waving others on when the right thing was too close to call.
Well done, boys.

A week ago, I was in my car, stopped at this same intersection. The
sun was bright and warm, despite the calendar and clock's mutual
assurances that it was a winter morning. Geddy Lee and the rest of
the Rush boys were belting out "Tom Sawyer" in the private concert I
held in my ancient, dark blue BMW 2002. I was right there with The
Holy Triumvirate, turning my steering wheel into Neal Peart's famed
drum kit. *Bang bang bangbang! (bang bang) Bang bang bangbang! (bang
bang) Bang bang bangbang! (bang bang)* And on it went.

Rush was kryptonite. Their music made me weak, and all abilities
to remain civilized were lost. The start of any Rush song required an
impulsive and immediate cranking up of the volume. Windows must

rattle! The steering wheel must be pounded! And early in the morning, humanity must be awakened! *Bang bang bangbang!*

Busted. My friend Max was laughing in the car to my left. This was my favorite part of living in a small town. Sometimes. Other times my least favorite. I guess it depended upon who I saw, but it was impossible to go through a day without seeing someone familiar. I was happy to see Max. I rolled down my window and turned it up even louder. He joined in, singing at the top of his lungs and wailing on the steering wheel of his pristine, perfect SUV. Our version of car karaoke.

Some impatient asshole honked as Max and I rocked out. I waved my apologies and drove on. Moments later, the offended honker sped past me and gave me the finger. I could only laugh. *It's okay, dude. I know you. I used to be you.* Not this day, though. It was my birthday, and I was already having the day of my life. After nearly fifty years, I was determined to live my perfect day. To borrow from Thoreau, I was going to live the life I had imagined . . . for the first time ever.

For as long as I could remember, I had asked my friends to describe their perfect days. Most couldn't do it. They couldn't wrap their heads around the idea of not worrying about money. They couldn't let go of their perceived reality. "What's the point?" was offered as an answer more than once. I never had that problem. I could rattle off my perfect day with ease. Sweat. Write. Fuck. Have deep, meaningful discussions. Fuck some more. Write some more. See live music. Eat good food. And fuck.

While some might think that the particulars of the perfect day change over time, mine never did. From the first time I thought about this day, which was probably some time in my twenties after selling my soul to start my career, the list of activities stayed the same. Still, I had only ever talked about it. On this day? No more talking. Only doing. I was going to live the life I imagined. All of it. And a perfect day needed to start with a perfect morning.

Before jamming with Max and being flipped off by the impatient guy, I had woken up early and gone for a leisurely run on the local mountain trails. (Sweat: check.) Six, maybe seven miles of a sunrise-painted, moving meditation. I'm not sure how long it took, and, for once, I didn't care. I ignored the self-loathing I typically experienced as my average time per mile slowed enough to blur the line between jogging and walking. Instead, I was in every moment of the movement. I noticed the rocks, trees, squirrels, and roots. I had a conversation with the creek running alongside me. The water talked back with encouragement, and time flew by. Even if I no longer did.

Following my run, I walked through the back door of my rented, tiny, two-story guesthouse that sat in the woods on the corner of a massive estate, which was rumored to be owned by some dotcom zillionaire. I never met the guy, but I heard he sold his first company when he was still in college.

His estate was built on multiple lots and managed not to be terribly ostentatious. It was huge, but tasteful. The tennis court, pool, basketball court, manicured grounds, and ten-thousand-plus-square-foot house were built neatly into the environment. Kudos to the architect. The landscaper probably retired on that job alone.

I did see the owner once. From afar, he looked tall, fit, and kind of normal. He was wearing jeans with a puffy vest over a hoodie. I was getting out of my car when I saw him heading to his garage. He gave me a hesitant wave that seemed, what? It seemed . . . I don't know how it seemed. *Lonely?* Then, with his choice of sports cars in the garage, he drove off in the beat-up, classic American pick-up truck that was always in the driveway. I imagined it was his first vehicle and a thread to who he really was or wanted to be. I could relate.

My own beat-up BMW 2002 was the same. I bet I would have really liked that guy if we managed to have a conversation. Despite our obvious disparity in wealth, I imagine we would have learned that we had a lot in common. That's all any of us wanted. Just to know that there were people with whom we had something in common. Connection. I wondered how many people I never met who could have been a good friend. Hundreds. Although I learned to honor the moments, it would sometimes sadden me to have a great exchange with someone in passing. *But wait! I wanted more of you!* Instead, they were gone forever.

Upon returning to the house, I was immediately greeted by the smell of freshly brewed coffee. Strong, dark coffee. Jess, barely awake, her long brunette hair tousled and falling in her eyes, stood in the kitchen wearing one of my T-shirts and singing along to Mondo Cozmo on Sonos. Couldn't wait to go to his show later in the week. A birthday present.

She handed me my cup of coffee, smiled, and wished me a happy birthday with a gentle kiss and slap on my ass. When I'd left the house earlier for my run, she was still asleep. *Good morning, treasure.* I went upstairs to shower. I wasn't alone for long. What started in the shower finished on the bed. (Fuck: check.) After nearly five decades on the planet, I had done this countless times with countless women. But, that day, on that perfect morning, it was different.

I had fucked women. I had sex with women. I had slept with women. The truth is, though, I had never really made love to a woman. I scoffed at the very idea. There's a striking difference between fucking, having sex, or sleeping with someone. Fucking, to me, was the most passionate form of sexual engagement. It was raw. It could be dirty. It was without barriers. But it could be deeply intimate and connected. As opposed to just "having sex," which was devoid of any real emotion. It was far more mechanical. Masturbation with a body.

Making love? That's movie bullshit. That's the kind of crap that ruined relationships. It just sounded stupid to me. Always had. I had never, not once, uttered the phrase "let's make love" to any woman. And if any woman ever said it to me, I'd go through the motions but know the relationship, or whatever it was we had, was doomed. I felt as though it wouldn't be based in reality. I couldn't compete with Richard Gere and Julia Roberts. I was no white knight. Plus, to make love, I needed to love myself. And that was completely out of the question.

But on this morning, as Jess and I fucked, everything changed. It was as though I found myself awash in a glow. Her glow. She looked up at me and smiled a kind of smile I had never seen before. It was a look of complete . . . "submission" isn't the right word, but maybe "trust"? Was it a look of complete trust? It was a look of peace. That's what it was. Total peace. No. Surrender. She was at peace in that moment and, with that look, invited me to surrender. To her. With her. Inside of her. *Let's surrender. It's okay to love yourself, Erik.*

It was a look that let me know that I was, for maybe the first time, safe. Whatever I did. Whatever I said. However I supported her, or even hurt her, which happened repeatedly over the years we were together, that look told me she was in for the long haul. It told me that, for maybe the first time, I could let go of the fear. I could let go of the pain that had haunted me since I was, I don't know, maybe seven years old. I could simply let go.

Just a year earlier, when a friend asked what I wanted for my birthday, I told him, "Peace." A year later, I was finally getting it in a most unexpected way. I made love, I surrendered, for the first time in my life. Not even Timmy would be told how hard I cried when it was over. For the first time in my life, having sex, or even fucking, wasn't physical at all. We fused. We created energy. We made love. I cried.

Jess never blinked. Never flinched. She just held me and let me cry. I hadn't cried in front of anyone for as long as I could remember. Certainly never in front of a woman I was seeing. Never after sex. That sort of vulnerability was reserved for the privacy of my own space and time. Usually in the front seat of my beat-up 2002. Sometimes with Timmy. And almost always in the most unexpected moments. Songs set me off the most. A reminder of a dark cloud that was never far away.

I didn't want to get out of bed. I didn't want to leave the house, but the perfect day needed to carry on, and Jess and I would be meeting again for lunch. After the re-shower, she forced me to get dressed. She playfully told me to get the fuck out of the house and again slapped my ass. I was in deep. And I liked it. I reminded myself not to fuck up again.

It was time to write.

When Max busted me banging out my best Rush solo, I had barely left my house and was on my way to the well-hidden café, Robby's on the Water. Only locals knew of Robby's, and none would dare tell the flow of tourists who rode their rented bikes through town about it. A lucky few found it anyway, and they were welcomed; but mostly this place was *Cheers* for the coffee-set. It was of the regulars, by the regulars, and for the regulars. Except there was nothing regular about the people who hung out there. They were freaks and weirdos of the highest order. The regulars at Robby's were outcasts everywhere else. And I was proud to be one of them.

I pulled off the road, and the rocks crackled under my tires. As always, I parked next to the fire hydrant. Local knowledge: it wasn't a real hydrant. Then again, I'm not sure it would have mattered. No cars were being towed from Robby's. I grabbed my weathered, black, leather backpack, which was filled with my laptop, frayed power cord, a couple of old, stained books, and the new journal and pen that Jess had given me after we surrendered and before she slapped my ass out the door.

I loved pens. I collected them the way people collected watches. A good pen, to me, was an invitation to time travel. With a pen, I could go back and reminisce, forward to dream, or even into space. The pen was a source of freedom. It could take me anywhere. My pen was truth serum. I couldn't lie when I used a pen on paper like I could when typing words on a screen.

I was wearing my favorite Fear Less, Love More T-shirt, old, ripped jeans, a battered Patagonia flannel, and my Red Wing boots. The boots were probably twenty years old, but like my car, the jeans, the backpack, the T-shirt, and Timmy, they were trusted friends. They had soul in their soles. I felt so uncomfortable when I first bought them. I wasn't sure they were "me." I wasn't sure I could "pull them off." Twenty-odd years later, I'm not even sure what any of that means. I worried way too much about shit like that for way too fucking long.

Robby's was the ideal place to be in your own mind-space to write or to strike up a meaningful conversation with a friend. And everyone inside Robby's was a friend. I suspect Robby's was the setting for more confessions than church. Robby's *was* church. Or at least what I thought church was supposed to be.

Unfulfilled professionally and personally and lacking love for myself or anyone else, I had stumbled upon Robby's several years earlier during an early morning walk. I hadn't slept for days, was stressed, disheveled, broken, and lost. I probably looked a little scary in my torn tattered jacket. I probably smelled equally scary. I had giv‹ for myself. At least on weekends. I walked into Robby's, and noʋʋʋy gave me so much as a disapproving glance. Instead, I was asked if I wanted coffee. Acceptance by caffeine.

I went back the next day. And the next. And the next. I started going every day. It was at Robby's, where I decided that I needed to find a new job. Cliché as fuck, but it was there where I finally admitted that I needed to find myself. Or if not find myself, at least acknowledge myself. Accept myself. My spiritual core was perhaps more instantly satiated at Robby's than any other place, and it made me want to feel like I did there, everywhere. I think it was the view of the water. Maybe something was in the coffee. Or in the souls of the spirits who called Robby's home. I didn't care what it was. I just wanted more of that foreign feeling.

At Robby's, I first understood the difference between *fitting in* and *belonging*. Fitting in requires giving up some small piece of yourself to become similar enough to others so as not to stand out. Over time, if you fitted in too much, or tried too hard to fit in, you lost yourself. You. Lost. Your. Self. You gave up so much of yourself that you became reflections of others or who they wanted you to be. Or worse, what you thought they wanted you to be. You no longer actually reflected yourself. I once read a book that appropriately described the ability to fit in seamlessly as a curse. I cried in my car when I read that.

But belonging was altogether different. It was magical. Belonging meant finding the people who accepted you. The places that accepted you. Wholly. You could be weird, and that was fine. It was wonderful. Nobody stared. Nobody judged. Better yet, they celebrated. Belonging meant that your quirks were just that and nothing more. I belonged at Robby's. Just like I did at The Gym. It had taken some time, but I was finally starting to feel like I could belong in these places and, more importantly, on this planet.

I never had a kid, but if I did, I would have wanted to leave him or her with this lesson—one of my "Dad always said" lessons. Go where you belong. Period. Don't waste time trying to fit in. It's way too painful in the long run.

Robby's wasn't a big place. There were maybe twenty or thirty mismatched chairs scattered about. Three old, ripped couches that would have been at home in a dorm or frat house were pushed together in a back corner. Tables were set wherever they were. There was no plan there. Nothing was permanently set anywhere. You grabbed a seat, you grabbed your table, and you moved it wherever you wanted it. Still, I always sat in the same spot on one of the couches. It was crusty brown leather. Ripped like an old convertible Mustang left out in the sun for too long. Duct tape "fixed" the bigger rips, but most of the scars in the couch were left exposed and each told a story.

The small tear on the round, oversized armrest where I sat was my doing. When I first discovered Robby's, I worked in finance. Every morning was spent trying to decompress from the previous day and simultaneously will myself to start the current one. I hated my job. I hated my life. And, after receiving yet another overtly passive-aggressive email from my Teflon boss, I unconsciously took it out on the couch with a butter knife. I was cutting without even realizing it. I hated myself.

Coffee service was self-serve, and payment was the honor system. If you wanted more than just the coffee, Val would take your order and Mo would cook it for you. Together for more than fifty years, Mo and Val met when they were just in junior high. In their early sixties, they took advantage of their right to marry as soon as it became legal in California.

Mo and Val's wedding was held at Robby's, and it was maybe the most beautiful thing I'd ever seen in my life. It was also where I met Jess. Or thought I did. Jess seemed vaguely familiar when I saw her at the wedding, but I didn't know why, when, or from where. All I knew was that I was done. Transfixed. While the other guests chatted with one another, I just watched her float about the room. Giving people hugs. Giving people gentle kisses on their cheeks. Every move she made seemed to have a kind of grace to it. She was completely present with every person she approached. As though it were only the two of them in the room. She'd take a hand or two in hers, lock eyes, and the rest of the room disappeared. She was hypnotizing. It was as if I were watching a play, and she was always in the spotlight. Only the spotlight was the sun. I couldn't look away.

Then, I lost contact for a split second. As I strained to find her, I felt a tap on my shoulder. "Looking for me?" I tried to stammer a lame response, but I was caught, and, for once, I just relaxed my shoulders and, with a kind of vulnerability that I hadn't known before, admitted that I couldn't take my eyes off her. I told her that I was sure we had met, and I was desperate to figure it out. She laughed and said, "I love that." She was interested and interesting as she peppered me with questions in our quest to discover our origins. She was compassionate and empathetic. A helper and healer. I suspected my eyes told a story of much pain.

She told me that she was an artist working primarily in mixed media. Colored paper. In a previous life, she had tried her hand at marketing, working for the big tech companies, but it just wasn't the way her soul wanted to go. She said that one day, she just quit and never looked back.

"How did you do that?" I genuinely wanted to know, as it was the very action I had wanted to take for years. Forever. She explained how she had learned to trust herself by jumping out of an airplane. I'll never forget this. She said, "I needed to overcome my fear of heights to overcome my fear of life." *Whoa.*

Jumping out of an airplane never had any pull for me, but over-coming fear of life certainly did. I was just about to tell her this when I figured out who she was, and I just blurted it out: "Oh, my God! I know who you are!"

A couple of years earlier, in that same soul-sucking job that led me to first-degree assault on the couch, a woman was walking the company halls with a kind of insane energy. I could feel it. She had a tape measure and was making pencil marks all over the walls. Wearing jeans and a flowy top, her hair bounced with every step. As this mystery artist glided past my office, I nodded and offered a comment meant to be charming, but I was a bumbling teenage boy on the inside. I'm sure whatever I said sounded like gibberish. I asked my assistant who the woman was with the hope that she was a new hire.

"She's hanging art," was all I got back. My co-worker never even looked up from her computer.

I told my assistant, "I could marry her." I meant it, but she just snickered and made a snide comment about my inability to get married. Then the artist was gone.

I was nearly in tears. I had no idea where they were coming from. She looked straight into my soul, took my hand, and never let go. I took a deep breath. Maybe because we met before or because we both agreed that we felt like we had known each other forever, I asked her to move in with me before the night was over. It's silly to even think about doing something like that. It was perhaps made sillier by the fact that she said, "Yes." *What did she know that I didn't?*

Jess taught me to speak up for myself. She taught me that being me was okay. She taught me that the mistakes I had made and the hurt I had caused needn't always weigh on me. "The past is the past," she said. She didn't want or need the masks—yet understood when I hurried to put them on.

I loved being lost in time. A nonlinear look at life that, from this view, looked like art. An abstract painting. Lost in a daydream about Jess, inside a daydream about Robby's and my perfect day.

A car honked and startled me back into "real-time." I jumped. Like being woken up during one of those super real dreams. You're just about to get a promotion, score the winning shot, fuck the girl of your dreams, or in my case, start writing what will become a bestseller, and . . . the alarm goes off. You wake up sad. *Damn, it was just a dream.* Even though you could have sworn it was real. That horn was as much a bummer as any 6:00 a.m. buzzer. I wasn't at Robby's. I wasn't with Jess. I wasn't writing. I was across the street from The Gym. And I was dead. Still dead.

I saw my friends walking into The Gym. One after another. Steve. Adam. Scotty. Jason. Kevin. Rob. Joe. John. Sandy. Andy. Max. Dan. Jacob. Chris. Doug. Andrew. Pete. The Pauls. Kareem. And Timmy. One thing I had become particularly proud of was the circle of men with whom I surrounded myself. Solid men. Vulnerable men. Funny, off-color men. None of them were afraid of their feelings, and none were afraid of toeing the line of political correctness. They were all fucking smart; they were all fucking offensive; they were all fucking beautiful. And now they were all strolling into The Gym, our dive bar straight out of central casting. Old TVs lined the walls. The few of them that worked framed the latest Warriors win. The rest needed repairs—for the past decade.

An old-school neon sign let passersby know that the place was called "Jimmy's." Named for its original owner, Jimmy's was more Vegas than Vegas. What happened in Vegas never really stayed in Vegas. What happened in Jimmy's was locked in the vault. Just as every local bar earns a nickname over time, Jimmy's became known as "The Jim," which gave way to "The Gym." Someone had stolen a poster from an actual gym about the importance of staying hydrated, and it was proudly displayed behind the bar.

The long bar stretching from the front wall to the back was original, and anyone who ever spent more than one night in this place knew better than to place bare skin against it. It was a kind of sticky that defied definition. It could tear flesh. It was a science experiment. Coasters weren't meant to protect the bar. They protected the pint glasses. The men's room didn't have a door, and the women's room wasn't necessary as no woman dared use it. The felt on the pool table was ripped; the neon flickered in the window; the drinks were stiff; and the beer was cold. The Gym was a dive. A dive's dive. Our dive. The Gym was fucking perfect.

I watched from my corner spot in the bar as Timmy ordered a round of Jager shots. Timmy asked the bartender, dressed in her regular uniform of a perfectly plain white T-shirt and perfectly plain jeans that perfectly showed off her not-so-plain, perfectly curvy body, if she believed in fate. One word, "Jendoyoubelieveinfate?" Although Timmy lived several hundred miles away, we had spent enough time there together that he was considered a regular. He had never once seriously hit on Jen, and she wanted to make sure this wasn't going to be the first time. She knew this evening could be different. She knew he was in pain. Pouring his shots, she responded with care: "I do, honey." Always "honey." Everyone was "honey."

Laughing, Timmy found his way back to our group of friends. All of my guys around a table covered by pints of beer, glasses of whiskey, and shots of tequila filled with varying levels of optimism and pessimism. One by one, they raised their glasses to me.

"To Skippy!"

"To Bernie!"

"To Bernsie!"

One by one. All my nicknames were called out.

I smiled from the corner as each took turns roasting me and sharing stories that were never meant to be shared. And most involving one sexual conquest or another. Doug told of my extensive video research project with his just-barely-of-age cousins at his first wedding. "In his defense," giving me the out, "they both looked twenty-five." Every story was followed by ceremonial hoots, high fives . . . and awkward silence. There was always awkward silence. Until the next guy started: "Remember the time . . . ?"

Then, the stories ran out. There was only silence. Nobody wanted to leave. Leaving meant saying goodbye. *Truly* saying goodbye. The days between the shock of a death and the service were difficult, but there was single-minded focus during this time. Mourning became all-encompassing. Real life was put on hold. Time stood still. No distractions. There were phone calls. Support. Arrangements to be made. In a way, it was easier, as there was only one thing to do: grieve. But following the service began a time when mourning was forced to integrate with the reality of a new normal.

Everything was the same, and it was completely different. This was so much harder. People were expected to be productive, but the pain hadn't lessened. It was all still so fresh. Too fresh. Too soon. And they were supposed to move on?

Impossible.

If they remained in The Gym, they could remain in denial. Outside, reality was waiting for each of them, slowly pacing back and forth in front of the doors and probably chain-smoking a pack of unfiltered cigarettes. It wouldn't rest until they were all gone. One by one, on their way out, they stepped to the bar and asked for a shot glass filled with water. It took a while, but they learned to honor the fact that I had stopped drinking. Like finding Temple Beth Am, it was just something I needed to do.

Truth is, before I stopped drinking, I felt totally out of control. Anxious. The world felt like noise. Billboards weren't two-dimensional; they screamed at me. I could hear them. I felt like Jim Carrey when he played God in *Bruce Almighty*. I needed to quiet my mind. I needed to do something that felt drastic. Something bigger than journaling every day. Something that required real sacrifice. Bigger than eating well or exercising. I started meditating and then settled on not drinking. That's the thing about finding any kind of true inner peace—if you're not being 100 percent honest with yourself, you'll simply just find the next thing and the next thing to mask the real pain. Not drinking wasn't going to fix me, but I was convinced that I could curb my anxiety that way. My friends feigned being pissed. But these guys were the best, and when they understood that I wasn't fucking around, they protected me from myself. On occasion, when I'd try to order a shot of bourbon, they'd take it away. I fucking loved these guys. I was going to miss them. I wondered how long they would miss me.

One by one, they ordered their water shots and placed them in front of my corner seat. And left.

"Goodbye, Skip. Love you, brother."

"Peace, Bernie."

"Much love, Bernsie."

"Bern on."

And finally, Timmy. For the second time that day, he called me by my name.

"I'm going to miss you, Erik."

As he left, reality snuffed out its last cigarette on the dirty concrete sidewalk and gave me a knowing wink. It was well after closing. The bartender with all her perfect curves turned out the lights. I remained in my corner seat, unsure of what came next.

CHAPTER FOUR

A boy and his dog walk the same route every morning for years. One day, the dog pulls the boy in a completely new direction. Although the boy tries to stop her, the shepherd keeps turning down different streets until they come upon an elderly man who has fallen.

Wearing my threadbare green-and-blue-checkered flannel pajamas and lying on the couch in the den overlooking the driveway, I tightly hugged my favorite stuffy, Pandy. Unable to bring myself to rise for a clear view, I hesitantly peeked through the dusty brown blinds.

I was nine when my dad carried our 120-pound yellow Lab to the car. He carefully loaded Blondie, her silky golden fur long faded to a coarse white, into the backseat of our orange, 1970-something Volvo station wagon with the baseball-sized dent in the driver's side door. *My fault.* A reminder of the time I tried to play catcher for my sixteen-year-old neighbor. One pitch. He threw way too fast, and I dove out of the way. The car was the backstop. I was lucky the ball didn't hit the window. Maybe I was luckier it didn't hit *me.* As my dad loaded Blondie from the passenger side, I could see her limp body stretched out across the stained canvas seats where my older sister and I always fought.

I remember thinking that I never wanted to sit in that backseat or ride in that car ever again. I also forever wondered how my dad was strong enough to carry Blondie. I feared that someday I would have to do the same thing with a dog of my own. *But what if I couldn't carry her?* It was a memory that was with me every time I thought about getting a dog or a car. Can't get a breed that I can't carry. Can't get a car without comfortable back seats.

Even through my heavy tears, I understood why this was happening. Blondie was lifeless long before my dad drove off to the vet. She hadn't moved for days, had stopped eating, and no longer responded when I gently stroked her face in the special way that only I did. First, I'd put my forehead to hers so we were looking into each other's eyes. Neither of us would ever blink. My nose would rest on her massive snout, and with both hands, I would slowly stroke the sides of her face. The longer I did this, the harder she would press her forehead back against mine. Regardless of how sick she got, she always pressed back against my forehead. Until she didn't. She was telling me it was her time.

Before leaving with her, my dad assured me that Blondie wouldn't feel any pain. She would just go to sleep and be at peace, he promised. He failed to warn me, however, about how much pain *I* would feel. He failed to tell me how, as Blondie slept forever, I was supposed to sleep ever again. Instead, he just gave me a hug, told me to "take care of Mom," and drove off. He promised to be back soon. My sister was nowhere to be found. Blondie was gone. My dad didn't come home for hours. I was on my own. If Joshua Tree was the first time I thought about my own death, Blondie dying was my first real experience with it.

A few years later, my grandmother died and I went to my first funeral. My grandfather's death soon followed. I remember his funeral because my parents let me wear my soccer uniform. I helped carry the casket as a pallbearer, proudly displaying my familiar number fifteen. I think I must have been thirteen years old. Then there was a series of friends who died far too young. Six or seven friends, none older than twenty, some as young as twelve, lost to disease, drunk drivers, tragic accidents, and suicide. In my high school classmate Alvin Ley's case, murder at the hands of a drunk uncle.

I didn't understand death. And I certainly never understood the ability to chalk up a tragedy like the death of my childhood best friend, Jond, to "God calling him home." Maybe it was cliché, and maybe a result of being around so many tragedies, but "death" became the natural answer to the question of what scared me most. Talking about death made me feel wise beyond my years. Thinking about death made me feel like an "old soul."

I was thirteen the first time I considered killing myself. Sitting on the end of my bed with a bottle of sleeping pills stolen from my mom's medicine cabinet, I simply didn't understand the pain I felt but couldn't explain. How could I have so many friends yet feel so alone? So lonely? I didn't know what depression was, but by the time I reached my mid-to-late twenties, those feelings were so much a part of me that I'd feel envious when I heard of someone dying young. Death was no longer something I feared. Life was. Just like Timmy said, I became an expert at deflecting.

"What a tragedy," people would say when someone died young.

I would nod in agreement while thinking to myself, *so lucky*.

I was envious because whoever died would never again feel stress, anxiety, shame, loneliness, judgment, fear, or doubt. They would never again feel disappointed. Never again feel pain. They would never again have to feel all the things that haunted me every day. They would never again have to question their decisions. They would never again have to feel like they were living a life completely different from the one they wanted to live. They wouldn't have to love from afar. Or risk loving right up close. I figured that by dying young, they'd avoid all these feelings and become legendary. Their lives, stuck in time, would forever be remembered in the most perfect light imaginable. Premature death has a way of enhancing a legacy.

It's too easy to blame it on depression, but somewhere, somehow, I became afraid of risk, afraid of passion, afraid of the things that made life worth living. Afraid of making mistakes. Afraid of myself. Daily, I fantasized about what might happen if I just yanked the wheel of the car while driving the high, cliffside roads near my house. Or maybe if I "just lost my footing" on a hike. It was always a solo accident. I didn't want anyone else to suffer. I was alone in this life, and I should be alone in my death.

37

To hide this darkness in my soul, I curated a kind of reputation as a great guy. The go-to for anything. I was there to lend a hand, an ear, or a shoulder. I was the one with the great advice. I was the first to volunteer to help my friends move or to reach for the check. "Let me get this," I'd insist. I'd justify how we were going to have years together, and they (whomever it was) could just get the next one. They never did. I wouldn't let them. It was as if it were impossible for me to accept someone else paying. I felt a kind of failure if I let my friends pay. Even when I was broke. Especially when I was broke. It was always in my darkest times when I wore the most ornate masks that fooled the most people.

It's weird. After years of thinking about it. I was dead.

I.

Was.

Dead.

I was gone. All I wanted to do was pick up another check. I felt guilty for leaving Timmy. I couldn't even allow myself to think about Jess. I suspected they all wondered if I felt any pain. I mean, that would be one of the first thoughts through my head if the tables were somehow turned. I wished I could tell them that I didn't. Maybe there's some kind of peace in knowing that.

In all the time I spent watching the cars at the intersection outside of The Gym, I'd seen plenty of people roll through the stop sign; few just blew through it. But occasionally, every now and then, there would be a guy. Always a guy.

Maybe because it was so late at night, the guy figured nobody would be around.

Maybe he was looking at his phone.

On those rare occasions, this guy never slowed down.

Unable to sleep, and on my walk to the trailhead for a late-night hike, I had stopped in the middle of the crosswalk to look at the moon. It was full. I was able to perfectly capture it as it hung centered above the new paved and painted road. I texted a picture to Jess: "A perfect moon to end a perfect day. I love you. Thank you." *Oh, God. Jess.*

That was there.

Now I am here.

Somewhere.

Not even sure where. Not sure how I got here. Like Joshua Tree, I was transported somewhere.

Regardless of religious beliefs, books about near-death experiences, or mushroom-augmented speculation, nobody really knows anything about the afterlife. There are questions, though. Lots and lots of questions:

Is there a heaven?

Is there a hell?

Is there reincarnation?

Can the deceased see what's happening to those left behind? If so, is there a time limit or statute of limitations on this?

Can those guys on TV really channel the spirits of the dead?

Do you reconnect with all of those you've lost?

Do you get to meet God?

Is there a God?

If there was a heaven, was it really all that was good?

Was I really sitting under these huge aspen trees high in the Colorado Rockies with Blondie's head in my lap as I stroked her perfect fur just as I had when she was at her best? Or was this all in my imagination? I didn't care. I was here, or some part of me was, and so was she. She lifted her head, and I pressed my forehead to hers; she pressed back. All was good in the world. Whatever world this was.

When someone died, we liked to ease the pain by telling ourselves that they would be reunited with other lost loved ones. I wondered if I'd find out if that's true. Maybe this was a big spiritual virtual reality, and I could see anyone I wanted. Even without a headset. I could make up any reality. Wouldn't it make sense that heaven was just that? The best possible you with the best of all you ever knew. Like your life's Hall of

Fame. But then, I wondered if the people *I* wanted to see wanted to see *me*. What if someone was in my Hall of Fame, but I was not in theirs?

How did someone already here find out that I'd died? Or maybe there could be multiple versions of the same soul? Was it possible for Jond to live in my heaven *and* his? Would our relationships be the same as they were when we died? Did relationships grow here? Did they know what became of my life after they died? Would I meet new people, or did I only find the people (and pets) I knew when I was alive? And, for that matter, what did "alive" even mean anymore? And my high school friend, Alvin Ley, who was killed by a drunk uncle . . . was that mentally unstable family member here? More questions. Always haunted by more questions.

Maybe time on earth was virtual reality, and *this*, let's just call it "heaven," for simplicity's sake, was the *real* reality. Maybe I was just a character in a video game, and I was now in some state of reset after losing all my heart points. True, it was a pretty fucked-up game if that was the case. Didn't seem very fun to play a game with a character who emotionally and spiritually tortured himself most of his life. And maybe the biggest question was, who was playing? Who had the controller?

My head was exploding with crazy ideas when Blondie raised her head, started wagging her tail, and, without warning, took off down the trail where we sat. I called to her, but she was gone, just like she used to be when she saw a squirrel behind our old house. I assumed she would come back. She always came back after a good chase. It had been something like forty years since I had seen her run like that. I couldn't help but smile as tears filled my eyes.

A few minutes later, I saw a man hiking up the trail with Blondie leaping at his side. I squinted to see who it was. Did I know him? From a distance, he looked older, with a scraggly white beard. He was thin, tall, and carried a walking stick in his left hand. His head was covered by an old fedora like the one Indiana Jones wore. He walked slowly toward me, clearly taking in the sights and sounds of the trail. He stopped periodically to glance at the sky—turning his face to the sun—to watch a bird or deer or simply to bend down to give Blondie a little pat on the head. She seemed to know him. I didn't. I had never seen this man before. He wasn't in any virtual reality of mine. Was I in his? How did he get into Blondie's?

As he got closer, I could see how weathered his face appeared. But it was wise. Like Morgan Freeman's face. I didn't know how to describe it except to say that he looked like he knew things. An ancient sage. A wizard. Like Obi-Wan Kenobi. His eyes were blue and kind. His smile exposed imperfect, stained teeth and immediately made me feel at ease. Without a word, he removed his beat-up backpack and sat down next to me. Blondie stayed by his side.

"Is this heaven?" I asked.

"It's not Iowa." He laughed a kind of belly laugh that made Blondie howl in equal delight.

He slowly reached into his backpack and handed me a white envelope with *Erik Bernstein* embossed on the front of it. He put his hand on my shoulder, smiled, stood up, threw his pack on his shoulder, and continued up the trail.

"Wait. Please. I have so many questions." I was begging. "WHERE AM I?"

The wizard didn't wait. And he didn't answer. He only kept walking. Just as he had before. Taking his time. Gazing at the sky. Down the trail he went.

Blondie stayed with me and put her head back on my leg as I opened the envelope. Inside was a card, maybe four-by-six, and white with rounded corners. It was designed with the same flowing font as my name on the envelope:

You Are Cordially Invited to Dinner at God's House.

CHAPTER FiVE

*A depressed woman attempts to call her friend. When an
unfamiliar voice answers, she realizes she called the wrong number.
They talk for hours about life and love. They laugh and cry.
They talk about spirituality and death. They remain friends until
the old woman passes.*

You Are Cordially Invited to Dinner at God's House.

I read this line repeatedly. Over and over and over again. I stared
at it. I read it silently. I read it out loud. I read it to Blondie. *Dinner at
God's house? What does that even mean?* I looked at her and said the only
thing that came to mind. Calmly and slowly: *Fuck. Fuck. Fuck. And
fuck.* She looked at me with her big, brown eyes and slapped a heavy
paw on my arm. She didn't care at all about dinner. Regardless of the
host, she just wanted me to keep petting her. When in doubt, pet the
dog. Always pet the dog. Everything will make sense and fall into place
if you pet the dog. Even just for a second. I pet the dog.

My secret hope for any afterlife was that there would be no more
questions. I had been haunted by questions throughout my life. Questions about my journey. Questions about my decisions. About myself.
Each time I couldn't answer, it left a hole; my soul was riddled with
these holes, like a car door in those vintage black-and-white gangster
flicks after the bad guys break out their old-school machine guns.
Questions nearly drove me to suicide multiple times and kept me in a

state of constant ideation. Faster this time, like that machine gun fire: *Fuck.Fuck.Fuck.Fuck.Fuck.Fuck.Fuck.Fuck.*

There was nothing on this card that told me when the dinner was. Where the dinner was. The card didn't tell me if other people would be there. Or how many. Wait. Wait. Wait! *God had a house?*

What would I wear? I hadn't even considered a dress code in this place. I was never very good with dress codes anyway. It always seemed like they were only necessary when I was at my heaviest and nothing in my closet would fit. I even had to rent a suit once. Not a tux. A fucking suit. That was pathetic. Pretty sure there were no suit rentals in heaven. Did I need to RSVP? How? To whom? I supposed I should be able to simply *think* my acceptance, and God would know to put me down for one. Or it's likely just assumed I'd be there. Who in their right mind turned down an invitation from God? Then again, that's exactly what I had done for most of my life.

Could Blondie come? Why did the wizard walk away? Why didn't he stay to answer my questions? Who was he?

Okay.

Stop spinning.

Close your eyes.

Breathe.

Think this through.

What if this *were* just my imagination? Just my mind playing tricks on me in a new and interesting way. The invitation. God's house. Maybe these things were all merely virtual and not real. Maybe they were nothing more than my deep, unconscious soul finding a way to the surface, into the light, via this heavenly VR.

At various times during my life, I had written a little about God. In journals, mostly, while trying to reconcile my depression or figure out why so many friends were dying. I wondered who and what God was. I wondered what meeting this spirit might be like. But I hadn't given any real consideration to being invited to dinner with him—him? Her? It? I don't know. That was too much for me to figure out. I was now talking out loud and explaining all of this to Blondie who seemed to be listening to me with her head cocked. *Did she just nod at me? I swear she just nodded at me.*

As I babbled on and on to Blondie, who was likely becoming just as sick of my questions as I was, I stumbled upon what might be an answer. Of course, it was in the form of a question. Was this a test of faith? *Yes,* I told her, *this was just a test of faith.* Faith. Capital "F." That had to be it. This was a test. Maybe I was not even in heaven yet. First, I had to pass this test. But how? What did it mean to pass?

Faith was also convoluted and elusive for me. Faith in myself was all but impossible to accept. Faith in some kind of God had always been wrapped up and confused with religion. I didn't understand religion. I felt like religion wanted to put my experiences in a one-size-fits-all box. It wanted me to act a certain way. It wanted me to *react* in a certain way. I felt like it wanted to make me feel bad when I didn't. But, still, throughout my life, even if I didn't ever speak about it publicly, I felt a pull, a kind of longing to believe in God.

I wanted to have faith in God. Some kind of God. I just didn't know how without having to buy into the religion part. I felt like faith could come with a kind of culture and artistry. Faith could be spiritual and flexible. Religion just came with rules. Faith, I felt, could give me freedom of imagination and expression. It allowed for mistakes and forgiveness. If religion weighed me down, I felt that faith could give me wings. When there were no answers, "just have faith" was a magnificent prayer. But faith in what? In whom?

I secretly pined for the kind of faith that some of my friends had. The kind that gave them a sort of "no worries" attitude about the most difficult times and decisions. "God's will," they would tell me, like it was a giant security blanket that could cover all situations. An answer to any question at any time. How were you able to quit your job and put your family's financial future at risk? God's will. How were you able to stay at that horrible job even though you hated it? God's will. How can you justify the most unspeakably horrible and tragic accidents? God's will. Never in doubt . . . Just go God. I'd visit my friends in the South where life just felt so easy. It was all in God's hands. God's will.

Still, even if it seemed easy, I didn't like this option. I needed to draw a line of sorts in the sand. For some, God is the *only* answer to *any* question. As much as I wanted that security blanket when I needed it, I couldn't justify this type of thinking. This faith felt blind. Blinded by religion. And, for me, that was going too far.

I remember discussing faith with a close colleague when she challenged me. Deeply religious, she asked, "Why don't you believe in Jesus? He was a real man."

At the time, her faith not only felt blind to me but also deaf. It was unable to hear any other viewpoints. Ignoring the whole Jewish thing, feeling judged and defensive, and knowing she was fiercely far right on the political spectrum, I countered with, "You don't believe in President Obama. He's a real man."

Want to kill a friendship? Start talking politics and religion. Her husband stepped in to quickly end the conversation by asking where we wanted to go to eat. Southern BBQ and sweet tea trumped God and politics.

Prior to this near battle, I had gone to a Sunday service with this friend and her husband. Their church was an enormous converted megastore. Aisle five was now kids' face-painting instead of hardware. Before entering the sanctuary, I felt like I was in Jesus-land. There were photographers taking family pictures. There were huge, multicolored balloons everywhere. Kids ran around as though they were in a Disney movie. Laughing. Playing. Music blasted from what I assumed was the kind of sound system you'd only find at the best concert venues. People greeted each other with hugs and smiles. Uplifting Bible quotes had been painted on the walls. It felt like *this* was the happiest place on earth. It was difficult not to be overwhelmed with the spirit. I totally got it. More faith-flavored Kool-Aid, please.

As we stepped foot into the sanctuary, I was told the congregation numbered in the tens of thousands. Well over a thousand would be attending the service in person with thousands more tuning in for the live stream that was produced from a control room built by a network-TV veteran executive. *Ready camera two. Go camera two. Cue God.* A live band greeted us with country Christian rock. I was in the spiritual zone. My mind was open—even as I was skeptical of the religion.

The pastor of that huge Southern Baptist congregation threw me a curveball when he said that religion was designed to make us feel bad about ourselves. He said that Jesus didn't want us to feel like shit. No, maybe those weren't his *exact* words, but that was the gist. I loved that message. I was ready to sign up to watch the Sunday streams when I returned home. Still, when I tried explaining to my friend that I thought her pastor was awesome, she brought it straight back to religion. She heard a totally different message. She felt that I needed to believe in Jesus to believe in God and that faith without Jesus, without *her* God and *her* religion, was meaningless. I was all for her having her beliefs, but why wasn't it okay for me to have mine?

At the Southern-BBQ joint, we were sitting with a member of the local college football team. He was a hulking guy with a forearm bigger than my thigh. Probably an offensive lineman. I wanted to ask him about the athletes who thanked Jesus after a victory or an actor who thanked God after winning an award. Does this mean that God wanted that team or actor to win more than others? Were the deeply religious athletes on the other team thanking God for the loss because that also was God's will? Was it really God who caused that fumble? What did faith mean to them? Was it better luck next week or next time? Or keep working hard and your day will come? Maybe I can ask God about that at dinner. *Hey, my dude, which* are *your favorite teams?*

Yet, as I was leaving my friends in the South when it came time to fly back to California, I did what I always did whenever I boarded an airplane. I prayed. I closed my eyes and made my silent deal with a God I didn't know or couldn't define. *Dear God: Please deliver us safely. If not for me, please do it for the babies and young families on this plane with me.* Or something like that. This prayer was repeated on take-offs, landings, and especially during turbulence. I know it was totally passive-aggressive. *Fine if you don't want to save me, but please save the women and children.* My hope was that it was easier for God to save us all in one fell swoop.

Flights weren't the only time I regularly prayed. Once a year, I went on a weeklong backcountry backpacking trip. I always prayed on these trips, as every one of them included some do-or-die moment when life could easily become death. There were snowstorms, bears, rockslides, river crossings, and simply fatigue. Even as I thought about the immortality that would have come from dying in such a way, I prayed to live. I prayed as I drove past car accidents. I didn't make wishes when I blew out birthday candles; I prayed. I prayed when I meditated. For someone who didn't understand his faith and distanced himself from religion, I prayed a lot. Especially on that rock in Joshua Tree.

But to what? To whom? And again, did it matter? Should it matter?

This was my "to be or not to be" moment. In absence of any comfort with defining *my* God, I sought to find some comfort with my spirituality. I wanted to learn to accept and honor it. I believed in the Universe. I believed in energy and its power. I guess, as I think about it, I had developed a kind of faith in that. But, still, I wanted more. I wanted to believe in some bigger God, but I simply didn't know what that meant or even why I wanted it. Or needed it. Was God the old dude with the white beard and flowing robes? Or could God be a young black woman, or any sex or race for that matter? Could *I* be God? Not in any kind of narcissistic way, of course. Why would God even need a gender? Or even a form? I felt I could only define my spirituality by better understanding my God.

It's what brought me to the temple. It wasn't the religion. It was the pomp and circumstance. It was the rituals that tied us through generations, creating connections and memories. I thought it could also help quiet the voices in my head that came with my depression.

I had tried to talk to Timmy about spirituality and death at different times, but he would have none of it. Timmy was a scientist in the purest sense—a surgeon who believed in death as the end and humanity as evolution. Survival of the fittest. There were no spirits, no miracles, and certainly no universal force. He wasn't quite Alec Baldwin's surgeon character in the movie *Malice,* where he declared on the witness stand that he *was* God, but Timmy was an unapologetic atheist. I read about a doctor who said the "white light" at death is just some brain stem thing. That was Timmy.

We once sat on the edge of the Grand Canyon shortly after I had graduated from college. Timmy was already in med school and on his way to becoming a celebrated orthopedic surgeon. I had dreams of becoming a writer, even as my inability to find "a real job" had me on the verge of spending another three months working at a summer camp. As I took a final hit of the joint we silently passed between us, the sun was shining a warm glow on the walls of the canyon, creating unimaginable shades of reds and oranges. The textures created a kind of multimedia explosion that artists try to recreate but never can. It's humanly impossible to capture something that's so far beyond human. I couldn't help but feel inspired.

"There's no possible way that this moment is simply the result of water, wind, and time. It's too perfect. This canyon was shaped by a sculptor that you and I will never understand. The river was God's hammer and chisel, but this isn't by chance. This is heavenly art. It's a vision that—"

Timmy interrupted me with, "—is created by you being fucking high. What the fuck are you talking about? Jesus Christ. Shut up. I'm hungry. Let's go eat. And I clearly need to get you laid."

No wonder I shied from expressing myself. While Timmy didn't necessarily judge my attempts to find meaning in everything, he didn't exactly encourage them. He tolerated and accepted them, often introducing me as his "spiritual friend." I wore that as a badge of honor. Even if he laughed at my search the same way my sister laughed when I told her Blondie talked to me. Only it didn't feel as mean. He just couldn't let himself go where I needed to go. To be fair . . . neither could I.

As a kid, I went to Jewish camps and spent a summer in Israel. I loved the bond, the brotherhood, the *belonging* that I felt around other Jewish kids. We were a community. Friends for life. But on one Saturday morning, I didn't feel like going to the services and praying. I was forced to go. Soon thereafter, every Star of David that I scribbled on paper included a question mark in the middle. That was when the religion was lost on me and with it, the culture. Because it was all rolled up together, in one fell swoop, I turned my back on all of it. It was far easier to discount any connection to God than it was to have one. When I got back home, I refused to go to High Holiday services. I was far from a rebel Jew, but that was my revolt.

There I was, though, praying on airplanes and as I blew out my birthday candles year after year. And to what?

Still, over time, I'd come to think of God as a collective. I prayed to the collective voices of my friends, mentors, and teachers. I prayed to nature and the aspen trees in the Colorado backcountry. God was the moments when I learned important lessons about myself. God was feelings. God was love, pain, joy, and anxiety. God was anticipation and passion. God was my best version of myself. And, yes, even the worst. For me, God was all of these things (and more) mixed in a blender. That's what I was talking to when I was feeling scared, alive, and vulnerable. That's what I was speaking with when I needed help and gave thanks.

When I really thought about it, my faith came from these people and these experiences. They collectively created the energy source that provided me with the knowledge and power to believe. So when I prayed, I was hoping that one of these voices from my past would be awakened to respond and remind me that I had made it through a situation like this before. Remind me that the turbulence—real or metaphorical—would stop. These experiences kept me alive. Even Timmy and his atheism on the rim of the Grand Canyon were part of my God.

I still didn't have reasons for unspeakable tragedies. I didn't chalk it up to "God's will," but I couldn't discount any existence of God or ignore my longing for faith simply because these tragedies happened. Bluntly, two-year-old babies were going to die unexpectedly. God wasn't my answer to "why?" And, conversely, discounting God's existence wasn't my answer to "why?" God was just there to lean on when it happened. The collective of my experiences was there to help me accept what couldn't be understood. The answers weren't in a book. They were in me. I had to learn to trust them. Because that's what faith really is. Nothing more than Trust. With a capital "T." I think the Bible said God made us in his image or something like that. Maybe it's actually the other way around.

But if that's my God, how can that God have a house?

Back in this strange, new reality, I still had questions about this dinner. If God were a collection of my life experiences, what would the house look like? I had no idea what to do or where to go. So I did the only thing I could do. I got up, dusted myself off, and got ready to walk down the path where the wizard appeared and then disappeared. *Okay,* I thought, answering the call of this test. *I have faith that this is the way to go.*

"Come on, girl. Let's go get ready for dinner at God's house."

Blondie let out a howl that I had never heard before. I think she knew more than I did. That answered another question: wherever and whatever this dinner was, Blondie was coming with me. As we started walking down the path, I kept talking to Blondie. "I wish you could have met Jess. You would have loved her. But maybe not as much as she would have loved you." As Blondie barked and took off down the path, I took a deep breath, closed my eyes, and tried to remember everything about Jess.

The smell of her long, dark hair.

The depth of her deep, brown eyes that sometimes looked green.

Her olive skin was like velvet to the touch.

My happiest, safest place was sleeping with my head on her bare stomach. In the grand scheme of things, we weren't together long. It wasn't perfect. Far from it. I lied to her. I tried to sabotage the relationship repeatedly. She just accepted it. And me. When I was over whatever I was doing or feeling, we'd simply talk about it. Or we wouldn't. It was amazing. It was the most adult thing I had ever experienced in my life. And, my God, did she support me. She had a sense of perspective that was unlike anything I'd ever experienced. She lived and breathed forgiveness. I grew up with her.

She wasn't perfect. But she knew that too. She accepted herself. How do people *do* that? I never figured that out. Her parents weren't good people. Her dad was a drunk and abusive to her mom. Her mom didn't drink, but she passed down the abuse. So, Jess never wanted kids. She was afraid that somewhere inside her was some hidden rage, and that scared her. That's why she started practicing meditation and yoga long before it was cool to do so. It's why she prayed. She was afraid. Except she wasn't afraid of life like I was. She was just afraid of a version of herself she never saw but which was likely lurking below the surface, waiting for its chance to be exposed. I never saw a hint of the rage. She either hid it, managed it, or it really wasn't there. Somehow, she figured out how to channel that fear into art.

I wish I had figured that out. I wouldn't have had to run from fear. I could have used it. Channeled it. Even though I was gone, I knew Jess would keep working on her fear, whittling it like a broken stick found in the wilderness. Before long, it's no longer just a stick. It's a tool. It's art. I liked that idea of turning fear into art. Maybe that's what singer-songwriters do. What writers do. What all artists do. She was full of surprises. Who was I to say that she'd never be a mom?

She was my happily ever after.

I kept walking and, after a while, whistled for Blondie.

I missed Jess.

CHAPTER SIX

A young girl releases a balloon at her grandparent's fiftieth anniversary party with a note including her address and a request, "Please return to Laura Buxton." The balloon is found two days later by a different girl, also named Laura Buxton.[3]

Although I loved the colors of aspen trees and the smell of fresh mountain air, the sounds of the backcountry were always my favorite part of a long hike. Among all the sounds, including the thunder of towering waterfalls, cool breezes that played trees like virtuosos, or the chorus of wolves at sunset, my favorite was the crunch of the trail beneath my boots.

On the trail, my feet became a kind of metronome, methodically pacing my journey with a measured, consistent cadence. *Step . . . step . . . step . . . step.* Each crunch of rocks, dirt, and leaves meant forward progress. Adventure. Each step was a reminder to stay present and marked a moment on the way to some destination. Sometimes, those steps were less about something ahead and far more about what I was leaving behind.

As I walked with Blondie, I closed my eyes and just listened to the duet of my boots and her paws. Her cadence matched mine perfectly, and our steps created a heavenly harmony. I didn't have a map or compass, and while I didn't think either of us knew where we were going, I could always trust the sounds. Listen. *Step . . . step . . . step . . . step.* We were going the right way.

I was overcome by the beauty. *My God, I love the colors of aspen trees.* This was my happy place. Even though I'd never actually been in this place—among aspen trees with Blondie. Even though I didn't understand where I was. Until now, I had never thought about one's "happy place" being less about the place and more about the happy. Because, in a strange way, it gave me the same sense of calm that I felt when I watched cars.

I remembered the first time I watched the cars. My mom and dad got in a fight, and I snuck out of the house with Blondie. Using the sash from my robe as a leash, I walked Blondie as quickly as I could up the street outside our house. The hill we lived on wasn't particularly long or steep, but to a pudgy seven-year-old kid with short seven-year-old legs, it felt huge. It was a daunting monster that I climbed every day to go to school, the local shopping center, or just to play with friends. Years later, of course, as an adult, I'd look at the hill and laugh. It wasn't as much a monster as it was a playful puppy. *Perspective. Experience. Growth.* Nobody told me that all the really big things would someday seem small. Exams. Performance reviews. Even break-ups. I had to learn that on my own. Maybe I never did. Another of those lessons that I knew but struggled to live by. The really big things would someday seem small. That is, except for my parents' fights. Even as an adult, with all those decades behind me, they remained huge. Especially this one.

At seven though, the hill was a monster. After what felt like an hour, Blondie and I crested that hill and began our descent down the other side. Making it over the top was always a source of great achievement. The feeling at seven was the same as when I would later climb 14,000-foot peaks on my backpacking trips. *Euphoria.* I always raised my arms in the air with the thrill of victory. Like I had achieved a great challenge. Soon after, we came to the stop sign at the bottom of the hill. It was less than half a mile from my house; but, again, in the experience and perspective of miniature me, I could have been miles and miles away. I was spent. Probably more emotionally than physically, but I needed to sit. I leaned back against the concrete wall of the house on the corner. There was a time when I knew the owners, but they had moved away. Blondie put her head in my lap, and for the first time ever, I watched the cars.

The first car to go by was one of those crazy, small, new cars from Japan. I had heard about them but had never actually seen one. It was light blue and looked funny. It sounded funnier. More like a lawnmower than a car. It was driven by a little old lady who had the seat pushed far forward and was hunched over the steering wheel. She gave me a gentle smile and a wave. I needed that. I told myself she was a good person.

I mostly watched. Sometimes, I'd wave if a driver waved at me. I began to make up stories of who was driving and where they were going. I shared them all with Blondie. The man in the yellow Corvette was a doctor on his way to perform a life-saving brain surgery. The woman driving the big station wagon was on her way to pick up seventeen kids from soccer practice. They would all fight to cram into the back, without any seatbelts, while the mom smoked a pack of cigarettes in the front. I saw a couple of parents I knew and tried to appear like everything was perfectly fine. They didn't need to know that I had run away from home. Three or four cars had dogs sticking their heads out of the windows, and I assumed Blondie was making up her own stories. *That one is going to the beach. That Golden is going for a walk on trails. Hey, I know that guy!*

I lost track of time as I concocted hundreds of stories. Then, I felt a great sense of calm and knew I needed to go home. I had run away for long enough. Still, with my mixed-up emotions, I didn't want to be a disappointment to my parents. I was born with an overdeveloped sense of "should," "have to," and "supposed to." I was trained to always ask for permission and approval. For anything. For way too deep into my life.

I looked up at the hill. The backside wasn't as steep, but way longer— like a dragon's back. As Blondie and I walked home, I didn't know the names of the feelings then, but I was anxious and skeptical. I just thought I was nervous. *What are we going back to? Is my dad home? Are my parents still fighting?*

Step . . . step . . . step . . . step.

The crunch of the aspen leaves gently eased me back to reality. Or whatever this was. Wherever I was. I don't know how long Blondie and I had been walking or how long I was in this memory. Like I said, sometimes the trail was far more about trying to leave something behind. That's exactly how I felt.

Up ahead, I saw a house.

CHAPTER SEVEN

While American novelist Anne Parrish is browsing bookstores in Paris in the 1920s, she comes upon a book that was one of her childhood favorites: Jack Frost and Other Stories. *Her husband opens it and finds the inscription: "Anne Parrish, 209 N. Weber Street, Colorado Springs."*[4]

I hadn't noticed the house until we were nearly upon it. It felt vaguely familiar, but I couldn't quite place it. Obviously, I had never been here, but I still couldn't shake the feeling. *Have I been here? I swear . . .* It was déjà vu. Blondie didn't seem to feel the same way I did. She gave no indication that she had ever seen this house and eagerly sniffed everything she could. With an enthusiastic squat, she declared the flowerbed just off the front of the driveway to be hers. It takes a special kind of confidence to pee on God's flowers.

It was classically Tuscan with thousands of perfectly placed clay roof tiles and painted in that burnt orange color that only looks right on a house like that. *What is that color, anyway? It probably has some strange name on the paint swatch.* I always wondered who came up with those color names. What kind of drugs were required to tell the difference between one hundred shades of yellow? Much less name them all? My version of hell would be sitting in a room full of expectant mothers trying to help them figure out what color to paint the baby's room. "IT'S YELLOW! IT'S FUCKING YELLOW! And that? IT'S

LIGHT BLUE!" *What kind of a sick fuck invents one hundred shades of yellow? Sadist.*

I did love Tuscan Orange, or whatever it was called. Like a perfect song, it was a color that inspired memories. Like sunset. That color was on Jess's favorite house. Every time we'd walk by it, she'd say how much she wanted us to go to Italy. It reminded her of her childhood, when Tuscan houses lifted her out of the pain of her reality. For her, walking by Tuscan houses was kind of like me watching the cars. It was an escape. She wanted to see Tuscan Orange in Tuscany. We had plans. As I swam in the color, I got lost thinking about the long nights she and I would stay up researching all the things we were going to do together.

Oh, Jess. What was she doing now? How was she doing? I was not even completely sure how long I'd been gone. Did she remember me? Did she ever get in touch with Timmy? It is amazing what a color can do. Or a sound. A song. Or a smell. Our senses are pathways to our past. Good or bad.

I still couldn't remember why I recognized this house. There was something about it that I just couldn't place. I had a feeling it was going to make me crazy. Things like that always made me crazy. Four huge Italian columns supported an enormous second-story deck that covered an imposing front entrance. A rose-tree-lined Italian marble pathway led to front doors that appeared to be made from an entire forest. The landscaping around the circular drive was so perfect; it was inspiring. I didn't know how else to describe it. I didn't have the words. It was so beautiful in its perfection that it made me want to be a better person. The mix of reds, oranges, greens, and yellows created living canvases worthy of Van Gogh, O'Keefe, and Warhol.

Was this God's house?

We stood in the circular driveway and noticed a handful of people scattered on the deck above us. They waved and beckoned us to come up. All smiles and laughter. Drinks in hand.

"Blondie, I've a feeling we're not in Colorado anymore."

We made our way to the front door where I hesitantly reached for the antique-looking brass knocker. I held it gently in my hand. *Smooth.*

Cold. Inhaling deeply, I looked down at Blondie, shrugged, and banged the knocker against the door three times. The door opened. And there stood . . . Ira?

I was speechless. Just as he had been in life, Ira was one big smile in a tremendously small package. Every one of his poorly aligned, stained teeth on display in all their inglorious glory. Meeting Blondie was perhaps to be expected, *but Ira?* Ira was the first person from my life that I met in death? Ira? Really? Fucking Ira? I could have listed a hundred people, maybe a thousand that I would have guessed I would meet before Ira.

Don't get me wrong. I loved Ira, but I didn't know him all that well. And here he was greeting me at what I thought was God's house. In this moment of absolute uncertainty, I was not sure there was anyone I'd rather see first. A perfect reminder that the magnitude of our presence in someone's life is often less about time knowing them and more about the moments shared. We didn't have many, but they were all real, raw, and vulnerable. Every single minute left an impression. He was laughing his ass off as though the joke was on me. Was this his house? *Waaaaaait a minute? Was Ira . . . God?* Seriously. That's the question that popped into my head. Strangely, that made sense.

Ira was a living garden gnome. He was maybe five feet tall. He had a long white beard and weighed less than one of my legs. He was like Santa. If Santa were the size of his elves. His teeth made the British cringe. When he wasn't lighting up a cigarette, he was smoking weed. If you stood next to Ira long enough, you could get a contact high. And if you didn't get high on the weed, you got high on his amazing energy and infectious laughter. I always stood next to him for as long as I could . . . hoping to get a hit of both.

A "reformed and recovering" stockbroker, Ira gave up money and stress to become a musician. He played keyboards in local bands and filled his time as an usher for a Minor League Baseball team. Women flocked to Ira. He was everyone's sweet, old grandfather. Their sweet, old, *dirty* grandfather! He could get away with anything. Say anything. Do anything. Ira would never be canceled; he was just that cute and cuddly. Yes, with the worst teeth ever. I never got over his teeth. Have I mentioned his teeth?

Before Ira died, I had wanted to produce a project with him. The idea was to sit Ira in the middle of a huge park with a "The Doctor Is In" sign hanging from the front of a desk. Ira would simply talk to people about their problems. He was the king of perspective. He could turn any problem into love. We imagined a web series simply called *Ira*, and I expected it, and him, to become an international sensation. There was no doubt in my mind that *Ira*, the series, and Ira, the man, were destined to go viral. Ira action figures were not far behind.

Ira and I had met through a mutual friend but lost touch when my relationship with that mutual friend crashed and burned in a most inexplicable, extraordinary way. It's amazing the damage that two pig-headed mules can do when they individually dig in their collective heels. A simple misunderstanding destroying potential decades of friendship. After the relationship implosion, I felt too embarrassed to contact Ira. Still, I saw him a couple of times, and he couldn't have been more inviting. He told me to call him. "Let's hang out," he had said, but I was too ashamed to ever call.

I was devastated when I found out he had died. My devastation was made worse because I only discovered his death by looking at his Facebook page. You see, I had previously hidden Ira's posts to avoid accidentally reading something about or by my former friend. What a pathetic, emotionally stilted child I was. He had been dead for a month. I cried for a week. They say it's important to heal rifts. They say you never know what might happen. They say. They say. They say. Fuck *They*. I hate *They*. Especially when *They* are right.

"Dude, is this your house?" I said with joyful tears streaming down my face.

"No, man," Ira laughed and said with a sly smile, "you know whose house this is." He knew what was coming next.

I pushed him away playfully. "What? What about that breakfast? You told me that you're a fucking atheist." I whispered the word "atheist" the way people whisper "cancer." Technically, it was lunch, but Ira

60

always ate breakfast. Eggs over easy on top of a pile of hash browns with a side of boiled spinach. It was an old man's meal. He was adamant that there was no God. He was spiritual, but God? There was no chance that he was placing his beliefs into a box. Music was his God. Baseball his religion.

"I *am* an atheist!"

I cocked my head, and he laughed at my confusion.

"Well, don't just stand there, come on in!"

Blondie jumped up and put her paws on his shoulders. She was taller than he was. Weighed more, too. She licked his face, and he said, "Good to see you again, Blondie!"

Again? Really? What the fuck?

I was already confused. Clearly this was not a time to be asking any questions. I followed Ira and Blondie into a massive foyer. More Italian marble. More big columns. More big everything. A spiral staircase stood before us. *I swear to G—* I caught myself. *I swear I've been in this house before.* And then I figured it out. *Holy shit.*

When I was in high school, my girlfriend's mom was a real estate agent. To earn a few bucks, and because it was fun, I sometimes helped her with her open houses. I would get dressed up and serve non-alcoholic drinks to the looky-loos who pretended to be interested in the multimillion-dollar homes. I did this maybe thirty times. My favorite house was, well, this one.

"Ira?"

He stopped.

"Is there a hidden door just below the stairwell that leads to a private playroom?"

He smiled a kind of knowing smile that someone might give when a secret is revealed. "There is."

I continued. "And beyond that playroom is there another door that leads to another hidden room, which is a few steps down?"

A bigger smile. "There is."

"Is there a giant pool next to a huge lawn, both of which are surrounded by enormous hedges in the back?"

"There is. There are."

Holy. Shit.

Blondie barked.

I started to run though the house, pointing out room after room. This was the kitchen. There was the second kitchen. That was the biggest stove I had ever seen. Did you know there were four dishwashers in this house? And seven bedrooms? Did you know the primary suite had a walk-in closet bigger than three of the bedrooms? Did you know this house was originally built by an emancipated teenager who inherited a ton of money from his Italian grandparents, which is why it had the Tuscan design and so many secret rooms? *Wait! The garage!*

We walked into the garage, and there they were: three of the most beautiful cars I had ever loved—a convertible 1956 Corvette, a convertible 1965 Mustang, and a 1983 Ferrari 328 GTS. Apparently, it was okay for cars to have crazily named colors. Just not wall paint. The Corvette wasn't just white; it was Polo White. Baby blue didn't do justice in describing the Mustang, it was Arcadian Blue. And the Ferrari wasn't red; it was Rosso Corsa Red. These three cars were red, white, and blue, and they perfectly represented the dreams of a young, all-American boy. They took my breath away.

Sometimes, I enjoyed watching parked cars too.

My excitement was short-lived. When I stood in this garage more than forty years ago, I had huge dreams. I was going to be a writer or find my way onto the cast of *Saturday Night Live.* I was going to be famous. Those are the dreams of youth, as I didn't know to dream for something simpler. I didn't know to dream for happiness and authenticity. For permission. Or not needing permission. I didn't know my best dream would have been to simply dream of being myself and living *my* life. I didn't think to hope and dream for something as obvious as the ability to wrap myself in compassion, to love myself, and for a life free of demons.

Instead, I dreamed of cars. I dreamed of fame. And of money. I dreamed of owning a house like this one. I dreamed of making my parents as proud of me as they were of my sister. As I stood in that garage all those decades ago, I had no idea I would spend so much time struggling to find light. I had no idea I would battle doubt, judgment, self-loathing, and all their demon cousins for most of my life. I had no idea that I would go *years*, pretending to be someone I wasn't because I was afraid of who I was. I would spend my life crafting a perfect set of masks, always picking just the right one to put on before I stepped out of my house. When masks were no longer enough of a disguise, I invented entire costumes. I was dressed head-to-toe in whatever most hid my doubts and fears. Standing in this garage just made me feel like I had fucked it all up. *Nice. Self-loathing. Even in God's house.*

Ira took notice. That's why Ira was Ira. That's why I wanted to sit with him in the middle of a park and just hit the record button. "Come on, Erik. I want you to meet some friends of mine." He put his hand on my back, and we left the garage. I tried to hide the tears. I think maybe that was the point when I realized that my life was over. *Really* over. I suspect this moment of final reckoning happens to everyone who dies. There must be a moment when all who have passed feel this heaviness.

"Ira, when did you first realize that you were dead? Did you feel like I do?" I asked without any need to explain how I was feeling. He knew.

Ira was Ira. "Erik, for a long time I was dead when I was alive. That's why I quit being a stockbroker. I feel like being here is just a huge gift. And I mean *being here*, right here, with you. We only have moments. How we choose to live them or experience them is up to you and me. There's a laundry list of experiences to choose from. We can experience our moments in gratitude, in fear, in love, in opportunity, in happiness, and so on. I always felt it was up to me to decide. I learned that I controlled my life."

I listened in silence. I listened in sadness. I listened with the weight and dread of regret. I said to him, "I can't believe I stopped talking to you simply because I had a falling out with some other dude."

I thought to myself, *Fuck, Ira, where have you been all my life?* Great. Something else to beat myself up about.

After leaving the garage, we walked silently back through the house, up the stairs, through the master suite, and out onto the massive deck. I stopped looking at the details of the house as we moved through it. I hadn't felt like this since before meeting Jess. I was lost. Numb.

I didn't have much time to mope. A cry of "Ricky!" echoed across the massive marble entryway.

Oh. My. God.

CHAPTER EIGHT

Twin boys, separated at birth, raised apart, and unaware of one another for most of their lives, discover that they were both named James by their new families. Not only that, they both became police officers, married women named Linda, and had the same kind of dog.[5]

"Ricky! Ricky! Ricky!"

Among all the nicknames I had in my life, from Skippy to Bernie to Bernsie and even Shirl, only one person ever called me Ricky. I stood there perfectly still. In awe. Paralyzed by shock. Speechless. *He was here.*

When I was a kid, Jond was my best friend. Long before Bennifer, Brangelina, and other celebrity couples started doing the joint name thing, we were Jondrik. We walked to school together every day. We played Waffle ball in the streets for hours. We wrote songs. We created movies. We found his older cousin's *Playboy* and discovered naked women. We were inseparable.

When we were six, we pinky-swore that we would go to the same college, marry sisters, and live next door to each other forever. Even as mere babies, he was the only person who knew that the perfect external facade of my life only hid my mess on the inside. We were true brothers. Not bound by blood, but deeper—by souls. Jond was the only person I spoke to about that one fight my parents had. I'll just say that even at six, we knew we'd be connected forever.

When we were eight, we caused a neighborhood scandal by escaping from our rooms during a parent-mandated "rest time." After climbing out of our bedroom windows, we hid under the huge eucalyptus tree across the street. From our vantage point in the ivy under the tree, we could see everything that was happening in front of our houses, but nobody could see us.

We watched some dogs walk their people. We watched teenagers on dates. We saw lots of people driving too fast. We saw the neighbors on the other side of my house having one of their big fights. And as we loaded up on the Hershey's kisses stolen from my mom's not-so-secret hiding place in the kitchen, we could see all four of our parents running up and down the streets calling for us. They would come outside and call us for a few minutes and then go back inside. A few minutes later, they'd be outside again before giving up. Then, out they came once more. This went on for at least an hour, and we struggled to muffle our collective delight. We thought it was incredibly funny. At least until the police arrived. Two cars. Four officers. Lots of lights flashing. We were apparently missing. That was far less funny.

For years, my mom never missed an opportunity to remind me how Jond and I made the situation worse by changing our clothes before we snuck out. Leaving our old clothes in a heap on the floor meant that our parents couldn't tell the officers what we were wearing. I'm not sure what was worse: the fact that not knowing what we were wearing made it harder to find us or the embarrassment my mom presumably felt in front of the officers. When the cops asked, "What do you mean you don't know what your kid was wearing?" all my mom probably heard was, *What kind of parent are you?*

As soon as the officers left and our parents went back into their houses, Jond and I slowly emerged from our secret spot and snuck back into our rooms. Our plan was to pretend like we were never gone and to play dumb. After exactly seven minutes and back in our original clothes, we would calmly walk out of our rooms and ask what was for dinner. *What? Gone? Snuck out? Changed clothes? Us? We've been here the whole time.*

Our parents obviously didn't fall for it. We tried to reason with them. We tried to tell them that we just went out for a walk. None of it worked. Grounded was just the start of the punishment. We had to do extra homework. Extra chores around the house. Our parents sentenced us to months of "community service," which meant mowing our neighbors' lawns for free and picking up trash at our school. We had to go to the police station and apologize to all four officers. We didn't know when it would end. My sister milked it for all it was worth and purposely left dirty dishes all over the house. As did Jond's *four* sisters!

Still, when it was finally over, we agreed that it was worth it. What our parents didn't realize was that despite the extra chores, early bedtimes, and lost TV privileges, they had basically sentenced us to spend more time together. And that was no punishment at all.

Jond was born Jon. At seven, he decided he wanted a different name. He had started watching a lot of tennis and was enamored by names like Bjorn Borg and Ilie Nastase. He wanted a name that sounded "more European." So, he changed his name to Jond and wanted it pronounced "Yond." He let his teachers know that he was to now be called "Yond. With a 'J' and a 'D.'" It was as legal as a seven-year-old could make it. And if he were changing his name, I would have to change mine. He settled on Ricky, which was spelled "rik-E." I was still Erik to my teachers.

One summer morning when we were twelve, like any summer morning when we were twelve, I went to his house to start the day. The door was locked, which was weird but not unheard of. I knocked. No answer. I knocked again. No answer. I rang the bell. No answer. I went around the back. It, too, was locked, which was completely unheard of. No answer. Seven people and three cats lived in that house. There was always an answer.

I ran home to get my basketball and ask my mom where Jond's family was. Before I could get the "Mom, where's Jond?" out of my mouth, I saw her tears. They were different from the tears I had seen prior to this. They felt, I don't know, genuine. The pain in them was real, not blackmail. I don't know why, but I immediately knew exactly what those tears meant, and I collapsed onto the rug in our entryway. I could barely breathe. Hours later, when I finally got off the floor, I went to my room, closed the door, and didn't come out for a week. My mom tried to console me as best she could, but I wouldn't have it. There wasn't anything anyone could have said.

She talked to me through the door and told me that Jond had a massive seizure during the night and had died. Apparently, it was a genetic thing that had gone undetected. The words from the other side of the door didn't make any sense. Like Charlie Brown's teacher. Just gibberish. Meaningless sounds. Jond was gone. So was Jondrik. I never gathered the strength to ask any questions about it. Not then. Not ever. I couldn't even bring myself to go to his funeral. I did manage to ask my mom if his mom called him "Jond," which she refused to do before. My mom told me that his mom, for the first time, did, in fact, call him "Jond." He would have liked that. It made me smile. Even for just a split second.

Jond was running toward me to give me the biggest hug I had ever received. He pressed his bleach-blond hair, still shaped in a bowl around his face, against my chest. For the first time, I was taller than he was. He was still twelve, after all, and I was close to fifty. He was wearing the same Los Angeles Lakers T-shirt that he wore the day we sat under that eucalyptus tree. It was huge on him then. More like a dress. It fit him now. Regardless of our age and size differences, somehow, in this instant, we were once again Jondrik. Blondie went nuts. She always loved Jond, and she knocked him on his ass and smothered him in kisses. I turned to tell Ira about Jond, but he was nowhere to be found. I was sure he knew the whole story anyway.

We sat on a couch outside on the deck. Oblivious to the other people milling about, I could finally ask, "Dude, what happened? I went to your house; you weren't there and . . ." my voice trailed off. I was Tom Hanks in the movie *Big*. Older but a child. Jond was the friend, stuck at the same age with a better perspective.

"I don't know. I went to sleep there, and I woke up here." And then, forever wise beyond his years, "I'm sorry I had to leave you. I know I could have helped you." We both carried guilt.

He was probably right. He protected me. He did it in a subtle way that hid his intentions, but that's exactly what he always did. Immediately following our bedroom escape, he took a much bigger bullet. He told our parents that it was his idea. His parents were far stricter than mine, which meant his punishment included his dad's belt, or worse—his mom's. But he never let on. We were of the last generation that was routinely spanked (his mom called them "whippings"), and his parents took full advantage. He kept most of that from me, and, though the youngest of five, he also protected his four older sisters. Wise. Way beyond his years. Strong. Way beyond his size. If I were to ever be described as an old soul, he was an ancient elder. *Was he God?*

"Listen, Ricky," he said, sensing the sadness that started when I was in the garage. *Man, I miss being called Ricky.* He put his arm around me in the same protective way he did when we were kids. Even with our age differences now, it felt familiar and right. "There's absolutely no point in trying to figure out the whys, hows, and whats of this. It won't make sense. Not even here."

I thought of all the time I spent caught up in "what ifs" when I was alive.

Sensing that I was slipping, Jond tried to break up the tension. "Remember when my mom bought you the Beach Boys' *Endless Summer* album because she wouldn't buy you that 'demon music' from the Scorpions?" We laughed. Subtle, but there he was, again protecting me.

I tried to play too, and slipped into my twelve-year-old self.

"I didn't realize that heaven and hell coexisted in the same space. I always thought one was above and the other below," I offered.

"What do you mean?"

"Well, I'm pretty sure I'm in heaven, but since you have that same haircut, you must be in hell."

Jond shook his head. If anything was the bane of Jond's life on earth, it had to be his haircut. It was, quite literally, a bowl cut. Once a month, on the second Saturday, as he sat in his kitchen, his mom put the bowl on his head and started to cut around it.

I tried to laugh, but I couldn't even fake it. I just started to sob. How different would my life have been if Jond hadn't died? How different would I have been if Jondrik had lived? How different . . . *Wait.* Only then did I realize that Jondrik didn't have to die when Jond died. Jond may have died, but Jondrik could have continued in my memories. I should have gone to his funeral. *Damn.* I was just too young to understand that.

If I couldn't live for the moment all those years ago, I could at least try now. For the first time in nearly four decades, I was sitting with my dog and best friend. And, dead or alive, that was a huge gift.

"Is there a Waffle ball around here somewhere?" I asked with a sly smile and a sniffle.

"Oh, I get it," Jond joked. "You think, 'Hey, this is heaven, so there must be whatever we want whenever we want it,' huh?"

"Well, yeah, kinda," I responded, amazed that our Jondrik routine just picked right up like no time was lost and nothing was weird. And that it wasn't weird at all that I was nearly four decades older than him.

"It's not quite like that, but I'm sure we can find one. Oh man! Remember when we stole one?"

I was feeling a little uncomfortable talking about broken commandments in heaven, but since we were already "here," I guessed nothing too bad could come of it. It was the only thing I ever stole. And it was an emergency. We had a game to play with no balls to be found. I remember going back to pay the store owner weeks later.

On the far side of God's pool, with an ocean view, was a huge, perfectly manicured lawn. It was surrounded on three sides by an equally well-maintained four- or five-foot hedge. Just high enough to create a kind of natural fence and low enough to see over. Or, better yet, just high enough to create the perfect outfield wall. If you hit the ball over the wall, it was lost. So, we called that an "out." A home run was a ball hit into or onto the hedge on the fly. Much more difficult to do that.

To hit, we used a small replica LA Dodgers wood bat. *No idea where that came from.* Ira reappeared to umpire. Blondie roamed the outfield and was kind enough to bring the ball back to the pitcher without chewing it up too badly. Whatever teeth marks she made in the ball were used for extra movement on the pitches. A ground ball fielded cleanly was an out. A fly ball that landed in front of the wall, but beyond the big blue planter was a double. Just like old times. Except since we weren't playing in the street, we didn't have to let cars go by.

I threw that first pitch, and Jond crushed it. It settled perfectly on top of the hedge in center field. Home run. I was down 1-0 and couldn't have been happier. I felt the same relief that I experienced during my walk through the aspen trees on the way to this house. I had carried the weight of Jond's death for all these years without realizing it. I had somehow managed to blame myself for it. As if I should have known he had that defect. As if, because he was my best friend, I should have noticed it was there.

We have all these experiences in our lives that leave behind residue. Over the years it builds up to create sluggishness and weight. These experiences influence our decisions, which we often make unconsciously. Jond's death created a void, and in this moment, I realized it helped me build a wall between me and other friends. What if they died suddenly too? I think I told myself I'd never be hurt like that again.

After twenty minutes, the first person to wander over from the pool was another kid, maybe twenty, twenty-one years old. He was tall and strong with long, straight brown hair and piercing blue eyes. A model, maybe. Or a young actor.

"Can I play?"

I had forgotten that other people were even here and hadn't given any thought to opening our game, but it seemed like the perfect idea. Jond took one look at him and, without missing a beat, said, "He's on *my* team!"

His name was Will, and Jond was smart to take him. Will had played baseball in college, and he told us that he died in an accident just before his first professional summer league assignment. *Fuck me,* was all I could think, but no words came out. Like prison. The inmates always asked each other what they were in for. Sort of the same thing here.

We were soon joined by Lynn and Emily and Stan and Habib. Then came Ben, Ashook, and Chantal. It wasn't long before our game was the main attraction. We had two full squads, and our made-up rules gave way to more traditional baseball rules. Except for the home runs. You hit the ball over the wall, and you were out. We didn't all speak the same language, but somehow when we spoke, we all understood. We didn't all look alike, and not everyone knew how to play. None of that mattered. We all sensed that we belonged together in this moment. We all spoke with love.

The wizard was back, sat in a chair behind the action, and started calling the game like an announcer. He gave everyone nicknames. We were Shorty, Lefty, Red, Tiger, Skippy, Rex, Panther, Stripes, and so on. He found something we were wearing, something we did or even said, and it became our nickname. He looked right through me and called me "Hemingway." Best nickname ever.

"Hemingway steps up to the plate with the bases loaded. Shorty is on the mound. The Gnome gives Shorty the sign to play ball. She rocks and fires. Curveball. Swing and a miss. Strike one. Red is playing very deep in left field, and Rex in center looks ready for action. The next pitch is on the way and . . ." It went on like this. Every pitch. Every batter. Except for Will.

When Will came to bat, the wizard didn't give him a nickname. He knew that while we were playing for fun, somehow, this simple game meant something more to Will. He rattled off all of Will's actual college stats. How he knew them was beyond me.

"Now batting, Willie Johansen. Willie, a tall lefty born to school teacher parents, is a lifetime .348 switch-hitting first baseman from small-town Iowa. He looks at a first-pitch strike from Stretch. It wasn't until high school that Willie really started playing baseball after a concussion ended his football career. *There's a ball low.* He was drafted by the Houston Astros out of the University of Nevada where he earned

All-American honors. Ball two. That's two balls and one strike on the tall lefty. This is the first time he's held a bat since—"

Willie crushed one deep.

"There's a long fly ball to the deepest part of the yard. Legs is going back to his right; he looks up, and it lands on top of the hedge! Home run!"

Willie jogged around the bases with a huge smile. After he crossed home, he immediately found me playing third. "Thanks. I haven't taken a swing in a long time." How did the wizard know? *Was God messing with us?*

First Ira. Then Jond. Now the wizard. I was a walking conspiracy theorist.

I could have played for hours, for days. I think we all would have. But we were interrupted by the dinner bell.

As the others streamed into the house, my legs were frozen in place. I simply could not move.

CHAPTER NINE

A man helps a young, out-of-town couple with directions to
a nearby restaurant where he is also going. Something about them
sparks his curiosity, so he discreetly picks up their tab without
them knowing. The next day, the husband shows up at the man's
office for a previously scheduled job interview.

There was so much laughter as everyone made their way from the
field into the house. So many smiles. Hugs, hands being held, people
walking arm-in-arm. Just joy. Pure love. I wanted to go with them, but
I couldn't move my feet. I stood on the pitcher's mound and watched
everyone head into the house. I was stuck.

From my spot on the mound, I saw that the sliding glass doors were
wide open, and a line of people poured onto the patio and wrapped
around the pool. *What is inside? Why can't I make my feet move? Why
can't I go inside? Where are Ira and Jond?* Doubt and fear overtook
me and filled the space in my body and soul that was occupied by
joy just moments earlier. What if this was all just a big joke and not
really God's house after all? *What if I'm not in heaven? What if it is
just a trap?*

I had felt this way before. I'd felt it when I tried to write, and the
words wouldn't come. That feeling of fear was fueled by a question:
"What if I wrote something wrong?" Really, it was more like, "What if
I suck?" That kept the words inside.

These weren't the questions that kept my feet from moving from the mound. Based on the circumstances, I was certain that whatever questions I had were a doozy. Oh, who was I kidding, I knew exactly what the questions were. *Is this purgatory? Am I going to hell?* I'd certainly made enough mistakes and hurt enough people in my life to earn that particular trip. I hoped I had judged myself enough to be saved from that fate.

Why couldn't I just stay in joy? I often joked to myself that my spirit animal had become the Saber Tooth Tiger stuck in the La Brea Tar Pits. Why must I always question everything to such a degree that I become an unmovable object? Why did I let fear have such a strong presence in my life? And, why, *why* was it still here now? It's not that I expected heaven to be a cure-all—actually, yes, that's exactly what I expected. I expected heaven to be a cure-all for the problems I had in my life. But just like my breakdown in the garage before I saw Jond, my demons were truly alive and well. How is it that I died, but they lived? It didn't seem fair.

The truth is, however, I thought I knew exactly why I couldn't move, and it had nothing to do with whether I belonged in heaven or was going to hell. It was about the root cause of all the angst in my life. The core of my depression. The thing that always stopped me.

That first time I watched the cars, I ran away from home because my parents had a fight. One different from the fights they typically had. Sure, they screamed and called each other names. Yes, they tried to pretend they were "keeping it down so the kids wouldn't hear." But that one was louder. Meaner. There were more doors slamming and, for the first time ever, the sounds of things breaking.

That fight, according to the tens of thousands of dollars and hundreds upon hundreds of hours spent in therapists' offices, was the fight that marked the end of my childhood. I was only seven, and from that day forward, my job was to take care of my mom. It was my job to make sure that she was never sad. It was my job to make sure she was never disappointed. I was afraid to show any happiness. I learned to lie. Love became undeniably conditional. If I did the right thing, I got love. From that day forward, it was my duty to take care of *any* woman who was feeling bad. It became impossible for me to ever hurt any woman's feelings, even at the sake of my own.

This, of course, wasn't possible, and resulted in me hurting everyone. That was the day, long before I had any interest in girls, that killed any possibility of healthy romantic relationships. I killed any relationship that came with genuine love. *How can you love me if I'm not doing everything for you?*

It got quiet, and then I heard the front door slam once. My dad was out. That was quickly followed by another. My mom was out. The second slam caused two pictures to fall off the wall. They were drawings my sister and I had made in school. Hers: a meticulously drawn, perfect picture of an angel at the beach. And mine: scribbles. They were both done during our respective year in kindergarten. The glass from the frames shattered upon impact with the hardwood floor, the blue ribbon my sister's picture won at an art show now torn by the glass. The angel ripped in half.

Immediately following the second door slam, I carefully tiptoed through the entryway of the house and into my parents' bathroom. Blood was smeared all over the walls like a crime scene. Big wet drops were on the floor, and I was careful not to step on any of them. The scale looked like it had been detonated, and hundreds of its pieces were scattered into the laundry area that separated the kitchen from the bathroom. *That explained the breaking sounds.* There was a huge hole in the wall just below the light switch. *How did the mirror not get broken?*

Depending upon who you later asked, the blood was the result of an accident, which was Dad's story. Or a suicide attempt—my mom's. Whether intentional or not, some sharp piece of metal from the now-detonated scale cut my mom's wrist. My mom had thrown the scale at my dad. They both agreed on that.

I was in the bathroom for less than a minute. Maybe only a handful of seconds. It felt like forever. Everything slowed down. It's funny how a few ticks can measure a lifetime.

Slow motion gave way to fast-forward, and I knew I had to get out of the bathroom quickly. To avoid the glass in the hallway, I ran back to the den through the kitchen, family room, living room, and my sister's room. I didn't care that she would kill me for even considering stepping into her room, much less doing it. I slid onto the couch in the den to watch the drama in the driveway. Approximately two years after this moment, I would watch from the very same spot, through the very same blinds, as my dad took Blondie away. On this day, I watched as he took my sister.

My mom pounded on the driver's side window while screaming at my dad. It didn't seem real. It was like watching a movie. Her hands were clenched into fists, and she worked the window like a speed bag. *Ba-da-da. Ba-da-da. Ba-da-da. Ba-da-da.* I hadn't thought about it until just this minute, but in all the times I've replayed that scene in my head—and it's probably been thousands of times—I never noticed any blood. *Have I remembered this wrong?*

My older sister looked terrified and confused in the passenger's seat. *Why me? Where are we going?* She saw me in the window and gave me the most authentically honest, sad, scared, and empathetic look. Those few moments were the closest we had ever been. Without a word, it was the first time she ever told me that she loved me.

I was equally confused. *Why am I left behind?* Confusion quickly turned to action. I knew I didn't want to be in the house with my mom after my dad left with my sister. I quickly ran to my room, narrowly avoiding the glass in the hallway, and frantically looked for my robe, which I found under the pile of dirty clothes that was always next to my bed. I pulled off the flimsy, terry cloth belt, tied it around Blondie's collar, walked through my sister's room for a second time, and snuck out the back door. As I quietly left the house, I heard the front door open and my mom gently calling me.

"Sweetie? Honey?" and then less gently, "Erik!"

I was running away and taking Blondie with me. After we watched the cars, Blondie and I snuck around the side of the house and back in through the same door. The house was eerily quiet. I needed to see my parents' bathroom. I didn't want to see the blood or the broken scale, but I wanted to look anyway. My mom's door was closed. I assumed she was taking a nap. Perfect. I could sneak through the kitchen to get to her bathroom.

It was clean. No blood anywhere to be found. There was even a new scale. Same exact kind. *How did she do that?* After she woke up from her nap, my mom acted like nothing had happened. *Fucking weird.* Even at seven, I knew that was fucking weird. Had I imagined the entire thing? It wouldn't be the last time I was certain of something but still doubted myself.

Over the years, and on the rare occasions when my parents would talk to me about this event, the story would change. It felt like psychological warfare. Mental torture. Gaslighting. My sister denied remembering it at all. For me, it was so real.

I was convinced that all my mistakes, pains, depression, fears, and helplessness could be traced back to that fight. I was seven, and it changed the trajectory of my entire life. It changed *me*. I spent a lifetime trying to "get over it" and feeling like a total idiot asshole when I couldn't just let it go. Or at least let go of the effect it had on me. But having to take care of my mom took away any permission I had to just be a kid. Losing permission to be a kid meant losing permission to follow my heart. And losing the ability to follow my heart meant losing everything. I lost the ability to trust myself. To love myself. To believe in myself. Or at least lost the ability to learn how to do these things. This was the genesis of fitting in. The start to my art of becoming invisible. Without permission to be myself, I could only become the reflection of what I thought others wanted me to be. I was good at that.

The memory froze me in my tracks. It was like an athlete developing the yips, a baseball player suddenly unable to make the most basic throw. All muscle memory is lost. When some wounds refuse to be ignored any longer, they become paralyzing.

Standing on the mound, I closed my eyes and prayed. I prayed for my own personal peace. *Please, God, I don't want to feel like this anymore.*

Please. Please grant me peace. This time, though, I wasn't pretending, like my prayers on planes; this wasn't about the kids or the women. I was praying for myself.

When I opened my eyes, a little old lady stood before me. She slowly walked to my side, gently took my arm, looked up at me, and smiled. I wasn't very tall, but she was tiny. Four feet, maybe. And old. Like eighty-something, with the wrinkled, weathered, tan face of someone even well beyond those years. She looked like my old boots.

She introduced herself in what I think was Italian. Rosa. I understood that much. I told her that I was Erik. She nodded in a way that made me feel like she knew exactly who I was. And, in the limited Italian I had learned while Jess and I fantasized about Italy, I said what I thought was, "Nice to meet you." Based on the incredibly confused and somewhat pained look on Rosa's face, however, I may have asked her for sex.

Rosa put her hand on the back of my leg in the same way a physical therapist tries to teach a patient to relearn to walk. "Lika dis," she said through her thick Italian accent. *One step at a time.* Slowly, I started to walk. I was nervous and really didn't want to go inside. I could see everyone watching me and felt terribly self-conscious. I expected them all to have the same look on their faces as the girl in middle school when she saw my life-raft thighs flattened on the desk. But they weren't staring with pity. They stared with hope. They stared with encouragement in their eyes. They felt my pain, and I could feel theirs. Step by step, Rosa guided me around the pool and into the house. I still felt stupid, but at least I could walk. These were the first steps toward learning to walk on my own.

CHAPTER TEN

There's a small town square near a woman's house where her mom met her father and her sister met her husband. One day, she accidentally bumps into and knocks over a man in the exact same place. They are now planning their wedding.

I was slightly confused by the fact that I didn't remember this room from my time here as a kid, working the open houses for my girlfriend's mom. I hadn't even noticed walking through this room when we made our way outside just an hour before.

I started to ask the kid who I think worked there, "What happened to the wall that separated the . . . never mind."

If this were indeed God's house, the wall didn't matter. Having allegedly created the world in six days, God was perhaps the world's greatest contractor. Probably the last construction project that got done quickly and under budget.

Massive, ornate arches stretched up to the very top of what must have been fifty-foot ceilings. They were white, like the rest of the room, and carved with a hieroglyphic-looking design. Scenes from the Bible? I couldn't tell. Not that I would know anyway. I wasn't exactly a biblical scholar. In fact, I wasn't an anything scholar. Another regret. I never studied enough. I never did anything enough. Except "good." I was a fucking expert at "good enough." I never excelled. I didn't do the work. I didn't have the discipline. Well, that's not true. I was quite disciplined at complaining about the fact that my life wasn't what I wanted it to be. I did that often. And with vigor. I once read a quote while doom-scrolling Instagram that was attributed to Tony Robbins. It mentioned that most people are unhappy; they're just not unhappy enough to do anything about it. Talk about a knife through the heart and into the essence of who I was. That was me.

I took a deep breath and looked around the room.

About twenty of us found our seats at an enormous wood table. Like the arches, the table was also carved, but I knew these images. They were the natural wonders of the world. I sat before the Grand Canyon, which was so meticulously and expertly carved that I swear I could see the Colorado River running through it. I was tempted to spill my water just to see what would happen.

Timmy and I had once taken an ill-advised hike down to the bottom of the Grand Canyon. Ill-advised because climbing to the bottom meant we had to climb back to the top. We didn't have any food or water. Our plan was to just walk halfway down to a lookout, but when that didn't prove interesting enough, we decided to go all the way. It had been an undeniably amazing feeling to be at the bottom of the canyon looking up. It felt like perfection to put our feet in the river. Heaven. Or at least what I thought of heaven back then.

As Timmy chatted up a newlywed couple, I sat in silence. I first discovered this feeling in Joshua Tree. Back then, as I sat still on top of the majestic orange rocks watching the sun slowly start its descent, I felt a kind of awe. There was a message in the silence if you listened closely. In the years that followed, when I was on backpacking trips or paddling in the middle of the San Francisco Bay, I learned to love this feeling even more. Insignificance. I found peace in insignificance.

Anytime I was around vast mountains or endless water, anytime I flew over the Rockies, I felt insignificant. The hugeness of nature. The power of nature. It all just made me feel so small. It made me feel meaningless. If I were insignificant, well, it meant that whatever problems I had, whatever I was complaining about at the time, must also be insignificant. A mountain breeze could make my problems disappear. Gently swept away on a melody of leaves. It was why I always wanted to live in Colorado. I figured it would be impossible to forget my insignificance surrounded by the Rockies. The vastness of the Colorado River at the bottom of the Grand Canyon gave me the same peaceful feeling of insignificance. Nature was the Universe's canvas. A reminder that we were all part of something so much bigger. Somewhere, I imagined, some other being was looking at us the same way we gazed at the *Mona Lisa*.

I made my way back to Timmy and the newlyweds and found him writing their names and address in the sand. They had lost their camera and their pictures from the first few days of their honeymoon. Timmy had taken a handful of pictures for them, and with no way to write down where to send the pictures, he wrote the address in the sand and took a picture. When we returned home and had them developed, we promised to send them copies.

It was such a beautiful moment in its simplicity. I was so swept up by the beauty that I suggested that the couple—*wow, I just remembered their names, Bethany and Chuck*—not buy a new camera. Instead, maybe they should rely on the kindness of strangers to document the rest of their honeymoon. Doing so meant that the conversations they'd have would be as much a part of the pictures as anything else. As much a part of the memories. I told them . . . "Maybe you'll make friends for life with someone you meet." I remember feeling proud of myself for thinking of it.

It was a moment that wouldn't work today. It would be blown up all over social media, and the simplicity would be lost. Our narcissistic need to showcase everything would kill the meaning. Too bad Timmy and I didn't become their friends for life. I wondered where they were now. Would I see one or both here? I hoped not. I sometimes wondered if they were on Facebook. I never looked. Checking meant diluting the beauty of the simplicity. Not knowing let the memory remain pure.

Timmy and I said our goodbyes to the newlyweds and started back up the canyon. Slowly. Steadily. Painfully. Timmy puked multiple times on the way back, and when we finally arrived at our hotel, his six-foot-five muscular frame collapsed so forcefully onto the cheap bed that it broke off its frame and cracked multiple tiles on the floor. I couldn't walk for days. My blisters didn't heal for weeks. All we could do for the rest of the trip was sit on the rim of the canyon and smoke a joint. It was, without a doubt, one of the best memories of my life.

I was startled out of this memory by a server. "Excuse me, sir. Excuse me. Sir? Excuse me."

I'm not sure how many times he had to ask me to move before I finally did. A kid, maybe sixteen years old, was serving me a gorgeous plate of ribs and fries with a side Caesar. My all-time favorite meal.

We describe amazing food as "heavenly," but the truth is we have no idea what this means. *This* is what it means. Late in my life, I became something of a vegetarian. And while I loved eating clean and feeling increasingly healthy, I'm glad whatever chef prepared this meal didn't serve me root vegetables and quinoa.

These ribs were the best I'd ever tasted. Not just the best ribs, but also the best food. I'm no foodie, and I couldn't tell you a single spice that stood out, but I can say the BBQ sauce was unlike anything I had ever had. The meat was perfectly cooked and . . . I struggled a little with the idea of ribs. *Are they really pork ribs?* I mean, are pigs being slaughtered in heaven?

The other people at the table had meat, fish, and chicken. Cows. Lots of cows. I couldn't imagine cows were being slaughtered too? Someone had venison. Another plate was filled with veal. Baby cows were being killed in heaven? *Come on!* Me and my questions.

This actually had to be the best-tasting tofu in the universe, right? Or maybe it wasn't even real at all. Just some artificially manufactured concoction. Heavenly molecules pressed together in just the right way. Could have been rib-flavoring for all I knew. After all, couldn't God just recreate the taste in some other form? I chose to believe the ribs weren't real. Just like Dippin' Dots weren't really ice cream, but instead, were some magical creation. Like Impossible Burgers. Or how "I Can't Believe It's Not Butter" tasted just like butter!

Blondie lay under the table, her paws stretched across my toes for the first time in decades. She didn't care what the food was or where it had come from. If it once sat on a human plate, it was good enough for her. I couldn't resist and instinctively regressed into a nine-year-old boy. One for me. One for you. She ate half the ribs.

We were a symphony of utensils clicking against plates. Nobody talked, but we all nodded, smiled, rolled our eyes with that "holy-shit-can-you-believe-how-good-this-is?" look, and kept eating. Depending on the room, no talking can feel lonely and desperate. I grew up around a dinner table like that. Silent. Cold. Mean. On this night, the silence didn't feel tragic but instead felt hopeful. I suppose that's hard to understand or even explain, but the room was filled with such reverence. It wasn't uncomfortable. It was respectful. Multiple conversations were had with simple eye contact. *Yeah, mine is amazing also. I have eggplant. Liar. Nobody likes eggplant.* Not even God's chef could cook that mistake well.

The room was also full of anticipation. I mean, we were invited to dinner at God's house, but nobody knew if that meant God would be joining us. At least I didn't know. I assumed the same for the rest of the guests. *Will one of life's greatest questions be answered on this night? Will they all be answered?* I imagine that's what everyone was thinking.

Until . . . silence was replaced by indescribable and uncontrollable laughter when the same little old lady who had helped me get my legs moving let out a ferocious burp worthy of a hardcore biker bar. It was a shock that caused us all to put down our forks and knives and start talking.

I used to love sitting in a crowded room, off to the side, watching. Kind of like how I loved watching cars. I liked to imagine the stories that were being told. The intimacies being shared. It's ironic, but I think one of my happy places was hosting a party and then watching my friends engage one another. I wanted people to be happy, even if *I* didn't know how to be. For a brief time, I could feel good knowing that, in some way, I had been responsible for a moment in their lives when they felt happy.

I knew that people felt jealous when their friends became friends. Not me. I found beauty in that. I loved creating connections. Maybe it was a subconscious way of creating a future for myself. Maybe I knew I'd someday be gone, but my memory could somehow live on this way. *How did you meet? Oh, our mutual friend Erik introduced us . . .* I didn't spend much time thinking about legacies, but that would be a good one.

Obviously, however, I had nothing to do with the events that brought all of us together around the Seven Wonders of the World table. I wasn't the host. But the joy I felt from watching people quietly introduce themselves—post majestic belch!—was no less impactful and meaningful.

The people in this room were a mix of life. We were young and old and everything in between. The youngest looked about twelve and was seated next to the oldest, who was more like one hundred twelve. We were white, Black, brown, and all combinations therein. There was gray hair, black hair, no hair, and even some purple hair. Our clothes represented different cultures and ranged from high society elegance to, well, not so elegant. Some had played in our impromptu game, but not all. *Where did these people come from? Where did all the others go? Are there other tables somewhere in another room? Do those tables and rooms look the same as this one?* I wondered who was sitting in front of the Grand Canyon in another room.

None of that mattered because, on this night, we shared the most intense bond we could never have imagined: we were all dead. Talk about belonging! Whatever we did in life was inconsequential. Or maybe it wasn't. I started to wonder if there was a thread that brought us all together, like Jon Favreau's old TV show, *Dinner for Five*. He brought together four celebrities who all shared a common element, and they'd dine, talk, and smoke cigars. I wondered if we all shared a thread. Did we die on the same day? Were we born on the same day? Did we all own the same breed of dog? Were we all afraid of living? I wanted to figure it out.

I watched the kid across the table talk to the thirty-something, beautiful African American woman. *Oof.* I made such a huge assumption about this woman. She was Black, but that didn't mean she was African American. She may have been from Paris, Japan, or Mexico, for all I knew. She may never have even set foot in America.

I couldn't stop staring at her while I realized just how much and just how easy it was to put our biases and expectations into a neat little box so we can tell ourselves a story that is most convenient for us. What was that cliché? Don't assume anything—it makes an "ass" out of "u" and "me." I wondered how many beautifully unique moments I missed because I assumed some reality that wasn't anywhere close to the truth. Or because I was afraid of what might happen outside of that box. All because I was addicted to my own story. The story of a boy whose emotional growth stalled at seven.

The man sitting next to me tapped me on the shoulder. "Excuse me, can you please pass the salt?"

I gave him the salt and watched as he proceeded to all but empty the shaker onto what looked like fish.

"My wife didn't let me have salt on my food for the last ten years. Can't hurt me now! What's your name?"

He spoke fast, and in my deeply contemplative, meditative state, it was shocking, like an alarm going off during the deepest REM sleep. He told me his name was Mort, and like any man named Mort, he last lived in Florida. I had lived in Florida for a short time, I told him. I hated every second of it. Mort laughed without comment and continued his story.

He was seventy-six and had died of a heart attack on the eighteenth hole of his favorite golf course. "I was lining up a nice sixteen-foot Birdie putt . . . I would have made it, too! It was the round of my life! Hey, that's funny!" Mort was married for fifty-six years. "All of them to the same woman," he said, cracking himself up. Her name was Jeanie.

She was only eighteen when they got married against the wishes of both of their families. "They said it would never last. They were right. It didn't. We were only together for fifty-six years." There was so much sadness in the way he said it. For most, nearly six decades together was a lifetime. More than a lifetime. For Mort and Jeanie, it was just the start of their honeymoon.

Mort was a Florida Jew straight out of a sitcom. Short and balding, his well-fed belly was framed by a red golf shirt tucked neatly into his checkered shorts, which clashed nicely with his calf-high brown socks. And he wore sandals. I was falling in love with Mort. He felt like that awesome uncle who smuggled you a shot of whiskey at family events or took you to your first strip bar. I never had that uncle, but that's how I imagined it was for other people. I asked him how he and Jeanie met, and his eyes lit up again.

"It was fate," he told me without hesitation. For the next fifteen, twenty minutes, Mort Goldberg spoke without a breath. The smile never left his face. His eyes were as bright and soft as the morning sun. I'm not sure I had ever experienced anything like it. I was witnessing the embodiment of true love.

Mort was running late for a job interview. "Always a mess and forever disheveled" was how he described himself. He had lived in Brooklyn because every Jew in Florida starts their story in New York. His mom was yelling at him to get out the door. His dad was telling him he was a bum, and his sisters quietly laughed in the corner as they played with their dolls and rooted against him. He came from lower-class roots. He didn't have much, but he also didn't know what he didn't have. He said he had a feeling, though, that there was more for him to accomplish. More for him to experience. He said, "I knew there was a bigger life." His dad disagreed.

He made it out the door, managed not to kill himself running for the bus, and long before anybody was talking about taking deep breaths and mindfulness, Mort quietly closed his eyes and visualized his new, bigger life. When the bus driver called his stop, he opened his eyes, calmly walked off the bus without paying attention . . . and immediately got hit by a car. Jeanie was in the passenger seat. Her older brother was driving.

"And you were together from that day forward?" I assumed, having seen too many romantic comedies.

"Hardly. I was in a coma for six months. The doctors weren't sure I would live. You must remember, this was a long time ago. We weren't exactly dealing with the kind of medicine we have today. I'm just lucky they didn't pull the plug too early!"

"I understand, Mort. When I was growing up, my grandfather always said, 'You know why they call it a medical practice? Because the doctors are always getting things wrong, and they need to practice, just like baseball players.' My grandfather told me never to believe a thing doctors say."

Mort continued with a nod but was quick to discount my grandfather's skepticism. "The doctors saved my life. I owe them everything I ever had. I'm grateful they practiced."

I was dying to know . . . Sorry, poor choice of words. I was champing at the bit to learn when and how Mort and Jeanie got together. I was like a little kid on the verge of a tantrum: "Tell me, tell me, tell me, tell me!" He was about to tell me when the dessert arrived.

I dove into my carrot cake and again savored perhaps the single greatest bite of anything I'd ever had. Mort took a bite of his key lime pie. Key lime pie was the only good thing about Florida, as far as I was concerned. After leaving Florida, I had been in search of key lime pie that was "Florida good." I would order it if it were available. And I'd be disappointed. "Not as good as it was in Florida." I finally gave up on that mission. I wanted to ask Mort if I could have a bite after he said, "Oh, my God. I've died and gone to heaven." After another bite and with his mouth full, Mort, laughing at himself, said, "Truer words have never been spoken."

We finished our desserts, and as I pushed my plate away, I prepared myself to continue peppering my new friend with questions when the lights dimmed. In the distraction of our food and conversation, I hadn't noticed that the seat at the head of the table was now occupied.

CHAPTER ELEVEN

A three-year-old boy declares to his preschool classmates that he has met the love of his life and promises to someday marry her. "Just you wait." Twenty years later, he does.[6]

I strained to make sense of the shape at the head of the table. In spite of thinking that God was the collection of my experiences and need not have gender or form, I was programmed to imagine an old man with long, flowing robes and a white beard. My mind and eyes conspired to trick me into that picture. The truth is, I wasn't sure who or what sat there. The light was darkest in that part of the room.

I heard someone gasp and utter, "Oh, my God, she's beautiful!" *She? Is God a woman?* Another said, "I love you." *I love you? Why can they apparently see so clearly, but I can't?* I strained even harder to see. I found myself needing an answer. A truth, more than whatever perceptions I had, misguided as they might have been. I would always have been happy to be completely wrong if I knew what was right. Another lesson in assumptions, perhaps. *Fuck, I want to see! I want to know!* I saw nothing. At least nothing I could quite put my finger on. The story of my history with faith encapsulated in the moment.

Then the room grew darker.

Silence.

More silence.

I was holding my breath.

A single spotlight appeared against the stark, white wall directly in front of me and behind the younger boy and his new one-hundred-twelve-year-old friend.

An announcer's voice followed, "All riiiiight!" I couldn't see him, but I knew the voice. I couldn't help but smile and laugh. Mort also knew it immediately. It was the late Chicago Cubs legendary broadcaster, Harry Caray. I wasn't a Cubs fan, but it was impossible not to recognize Caray's boisterous, signature style. During his day, he was a permanent fixture in TV commercials, and his Chicago restaurant was legendary. Caray, Cubs, and Budweiser were a different kind of Holy Trinity.

Perhaps what made Harry Caray most famous, however, was his rendition of the classic seventh-inning stretch. Before the bottom of the seventh, he would open the window to his broadcast booth, lean out with his microphone, and fire up the crowd with a bellowing, "Allll riiiiiigggghhhttt!!!!" And together, they would sing, "Take Me Out to the Ball Game."

For most baseball fans, the song was a fun tradition, but for Cubs fans, it was a prayer. *Please, God, let this be the year we finally win it all.* Harry never got to see his beloved, hapless Cubs win a World Series in his lifetime. They came close but always fell short in some mysterious way. Some felt they were cursed. He died, and I suppose if you become God's announcer, that's a pretty good consolation prize. An indication that you did something right. As they say, it's not whether you win or lose, yadda, yadda, yadda.

"Ladies and gentlemen!" I still couldn't see him. "Welcome to God's house!"

None of us were sure what to do. Do we clap? Do we hoot and holler? Do we continue to quietly sit on our thumbs, dumbstruck? Maybe, just maybe, God was sitting at the end of the table, and that created a unique uncertainty and anxiety. Just what is the protocol in this situation? I didn't recall covering this one in any of my Hebrew school classes as a kid.

Harry helped us out, calling, "I *said,* Welcome to God's houuuuuuuuuuuuusssssse!"

That was our cue. We had been given permission to jump up from our seats and go nuts! High fives were everywhere. Hugs. Some tears, which may have been more about relief than sadness. This would, perhaps, be a fun night after all. I glanced at the shadow at the head of the table. Still. Like a statue.

Harry continued. "Ladies and gentlemen, tonight, in death, for the first time ever, you are going to be introduced to one of the great mysteries of life."

There was a buzz among everyone around the table. Mort turned to me and confirmed what I was thinking and, with both hands on my shoulders, whispered, "We're going to meet God tonight."

So it wasn't just me.

Then the room got even darker. One by one, a chorus of angels singing a haunting harmony, their wings glowing in a soft light, floated into the room. Slowly, they circled and created a sound so deeply nuanced, it was like they were singing emotions. Prior to this moment, I had equated happiness as sounding like laughter and sadness as crying. This was the same, but so completely different. It felt personal, as though the tones they sang were telling a story of my life. I could feel the highs and lows. I could feel the moments of joy and episodes of darkness. Heavenly. There was no other word to describe what they sang or how they sounded. They sounded heavenly. I wondered if the others heard what I heard.

As their harmony began to lighten and the intensity lessened, a series of colored lights began to spin around the room. Randomly, the red, green, yellow, blue, and orange lights danced on the walls, across the table, and even over our faces. The long, laser-like lights created a beautiful web above us and cast just enough of a glow that I could see the smiles, dropped jaws, and awe on the faces of my deceased friends and fellow dinner guests. At least, I *think* we were all deceased. I wasn't sure. Another assumption. I really needed to stop doing that.

"In life," Harry narrated, "many of us wonder about the existence of God. We wonder about the universe and how it operates. Even those of us who don't believe, or just can't find their way to believe, are often curious. There are moments for everyone when something happens that shouldn't have happened. Or something doesn't happen that should have. And we often chalk up those moments to circumstances, luck, or coincidence—good and bad. Tonight, you'll learn that most of these situations aren't circumstance or luck at all. Or maybe they are still just dumb luck. You'll get to decide."

My heart was racing. I could feel it crashing against the inside of my chest like it was trying to escape a locked vault. Harry then borrowed from Lennon and McCartney. Only this time, he wasn't introducing Billy Shears. God probably doesn't worry too much about royalties.

As he took a big pause, we started screaming like the studio audience of *Oprah's Favorite Things*. If this were a reality show like *The Voice* or *Dancing with the Stars,* Harry would have thrown his intro to a commercial. Everyone in the room was anticipating the introduction of God.

Then the laser lights started dancing across the wall. The angels started to sing again. This time, the lasers weren't so random, and the angels not so haunting. It was playful. Whimsical. Almost silly. Like the theme from a circus or carnival. The lasers were writing on the wall.

A word starting with "F." Another letter. "A." Confusion set in.

"Ladies and gentlemen . . . I give you . . ."

Next came a "T," and just as the "E" was formed on the wall, Harry bellowed, "FAAAAAAAAAAATE!"

Wait. What? Fate? Not God? Fate? He meant God, right? I looked at Mort. *He meant God, right?*

Before I could go any deeper into the series of questions flooding my soul and try to interpret what had just happened, a form zipped into the room. A blur. It moved from corner to corner. From ceiling to floor. It would stop just long enough for our eyes to catch a glimpse, but not long enough to figure out what it was. It seemed frantic. Chaotic. Random. At one point, I thought it was standing on the table. Assuming it was God at the head of the table, I thought the blur sat on God's lap. And if I was not mistaken, God laughed his ass off.

An audible "whoooosh" followed the blur every time it moved. Was it caused by the speed at which it moved or the angels singing sound effects like some kind of a cappella group? At this point, I wasn't sure of anything. A smile was plastered on my face. I guess I was sure of that. Whatever this was, the lights, the sights, and the sounds made it fun. Laugh-out-loud fun. Belly-laughing fun. I couldn't remember the last time I let myself laugh like that. Not even with Jess.

A spotlight was cast onto the center of the table, and there he stood— motionless but posing like a supermodel during some kind of absurd photo shoot. Dressed exactly like a court jester with pointy shoes, a multicolored smock, and a funny hat with bells, Fate, at least I had to think this was Fate, slowly looked around the room. He turned to look each of us in the eyes. When he got to me, he seemed to pause and cock his head ever so slightly, his piercing blue eyes looking right through me. He then howled a guttural laugh that startled me. *Why did he laugh at me and nobody else? What did he know that I didn't?* Things suddenly felt a little less fun.

Fate was short. Maybe five-foot-five, but he appeared to be in great shape. That, or he was wearing fake muscles like a superhero costume. His gear fit tightly over his body. His purple tights showed off well-formed calves. He wore a white mask with a painted expression that hid any true emotions. The ultimate expression of a chameleon. Someone who could play to any room. This single mask had managed to capture the entirety of my life. In the moment, it felt very sad. And that made me feel very sad. Mort tapped me on the shoulder and whispered, "He's beautiful." I wasn't so sure.

Fate spoke, "Please take your seats." His voice was deeper than I expected. Maybe I didn't expect him to speak at all. And the fact that his lips weren't moving was completely off-putting. He continued a slow turn as he spoke.

"I am Fate." He said it like Darth Vader telling Luke he was his father. He took a beat to let it sink in, then quickly, "AndIamyour-entertainmentfortheevening!" He cackled and again started zipping around the room. He was moving so fast that we couldn't even see the blur; we could only hear the sound. His movement caused an echo, and we all spun in our chairs and craned our necks trying to figure out where he was.

Where did he go? What is he going to do? Card tricks? Is he going to do stand-up? Some kind of vaudeville act? He stopped to show himself and taunted us with a higher pitch, still talking extremely fast. "Youghostshavenoideawhatisabouttohappen!" he screamed with a kind of maniacal delight that made me think of Robin Williams or Jim Carrey. And yet again, he took off around the room. The lights still swirling. The angels still singing. Blondie didn't move. It's like she had seen this before. I was glad I wasn't having a seizure.

Then just as suddenly as he took off . . . he stopped and looked directly at Mort.

"Mort Goldberg, you were exactly right when you told Erik that meeting Jeanie was fate." Fate winked.

I looked at Mort, mouth open wide. If my jaw could hit the floor, it would have. Mort, though, looked cool. Having his love and life confirmed must have felt comforting. His faith was delivered. Again, Fate took off. Definitely Robin Williams. He seemed to have that kind of brilliance to his madness, and that look in his eye that let everyone know he wasn't just one step ahead of us but miles and miles ahead.

One by one, Fate stopped in front of everyone and explained situation after situation that he had apparently manipulated. He told stories of wrong numbers. He told us about Billy Tevens, who sat two seats to my left and was apparently fired from his job due to a misunderstanding over a lost file. A file, it turns out, which was later found and resulted in a promotion and finding a long-lost half-brother.

"The file wasn't lost," he teased. "You were."

And then it was my turn. I was last. "Erik, Erik, Erik . . . You have been one of the most frustrating subjects I've ever worked with. The questions. The questions. Oy! All the questions. I gave you more opportunities to make life-changing choices than perhaps anyone who ever came before you. But you never budged. Do you have any clue how many different times you and Jess were in the same place at the same time? You talked a big game and then stayed right where you were. Your feet comfortably cemented in place, and your mind in its story."

I felt like a kid being called out by his coach after a bad game. I was embarrassed. Heaven had become my hell. If I could have traded places with Blondie, I would have. I had forever said that being my dog was the best gig on the planet. Turns out, it was the best gig in the universe. I wanted to hide under the table. Fate noticed my unease and let up.

"We'll get back to you."

Fate addressed the room. "Ladies and gentlemen, tonight I am going to show you who I am and what I do. The truth is that God has a difficult job," he said, gesturing to the end of the table and confirming what we had all hoped—God was in the room. "And despite all the love God feels, it's a lonely job. So my job is that of God's court jester." That explained the costume.

"It's my job to bring levity to the universe. It's my job to introduce people who might never otherwise meet. It's my job to create situations where you're forced to make a choice. Go left? Go right? Or sometimes," he said, looking right into my eyes, "stay right where you are."

Mort again placed his hand on my shoulder. And Blondie put her head on my shoe.

"Think about all the times in your life when you felt a kind of wonder at meeting someone. Reconnecting with someone. All the times when some set of circumstances created a moment that was inexplicable. It's amazing, right?"

We all nodded silently.

"It turns out that many—not all—of those moments are creations of my imagination. They are designed to delight God. To make all the people who have come before you laugh. They are experiments in the beauty of human existence and the human experience."

I couldn't decide if this was funny or more like seeing the kitchen of your favorite restaurant and discovering it was infested with cockroaches. Sometimes, it's not such a good thing to look under the hood or behind the scenes. I always liked the mystery of circumstance. I liked feeling as though chance meetings were random, and immediate intimate connections, a gift. But what if it turns out that it was all just predestined or truly just fated?

Mort told me that getting hit by the car to meet Jeanie was fate. But it turns out—it was Fate with a capital "F." To me, that lessened the impact of the moment. To me, taking chance out of the story made it far less romantic. If the whole thing was just choreographed, what did it actually mean? I didn't like feeling as though we were being moved around like chess pieces. Was there no free will? Were we just all puppets in this show? *Were* we just characters in a video game? Fate said that Jess appeared in my life multiple times, and I missed it. What if I had kept missing her? Were we "supposed to" be together? My whole life already felt like a series of "supposed to." I wanted less of that. I had blamed my parents for my struggles all these years. I blamed the fights. Were the fights Fated, too? Were we all just following a script?

I felt dizzy as I strained to understand what was happening. I wanted to leave. I wanted to cover my ears and sing, "lalalalalalalalalalalalalala" to make it go away, to make it stop, and avoid hearing anything else. I may have been afraid of taking huge leaps, but I was inspired by the people who did. And if they weren't real, what did that mean for my inspiration?

What about all of these supposed circumstances that apparently made the heavens laugh but brought me so much anxiety and suffering? Did Fate intercept the soul-exposing letter from the (then) love of my life that explained that she wanted to give it a shot? I never received that letter. And we never got that shot. Was it funny to Fate that shortly into my friend's failed marriage, he randomly and innocently reconnected—until now, I thought it was random—with his secret grade school fantasy crush and couldn't do a thing about it? Seemed to me that Fate was maybe kind of cruel. I tried to stifle the thought I had because it couldn't possibly have been more inappropriate at the time, but still quietly mumbled, "Goddamnit."

I looked around the room and saw smiles, laughter, and what I assumed was joy. I felt like I was experiencing something completely different than the others in the room. I never was very good at joy.

CHAPTER TWELVE

A woman finds a lost wallet that contains a "Dear John" love letter written sixty years earlier. She tracks down the woman who wrote the letter and the man who lost the wallet. They live in the same retirement home.[7]

I was struggling to believe that our lives were predetermined. Or if not predetermined, dramatically influenced. Which events were the result of Fate, and which were the result of free will? For that matter, how did God play into this equation? What was *his* role? Did he really give up that kind of control just to amuse himself? Could Fate, did Fate, influence free will by altering the path that I took? If I decided on my own accord to go left, and it turned out to be the greatest decision I'd ever made, couldn't Fate then drop an obstacle or person in my path, which would then force me to change directions and potentially end up going the wrong way? I guess what really bugged me was that I felt like I wasted so much time struggling to be happy. I spent most of my life feeling like I didn't belong. Feeling like an alien. If it's all just scripted, why would that happen? "God's will" was the answer to some of the most complicated questions, but was "Fate's will" just as prevalent? *Fuck.*

When things weren't going right, I had on many occasions asked, "Is this some kind of joke?" The fact was that maybe, just maybe, it was exactly that. And the joke was not just played on me, but on all of us.

It was more than I was prepared to handle. Or understand. How was I supposed to process this? Where were Jond and Ira? Did they know this was going to be happening? They must have.

I just wanted to go back to the woods with Blondie. Back to my virtual reality. Who cares if that meant I wouldn't meet God? I didn't know what that meant anyway, right? It's not like he was walking around the table, asking us all how we enjoyed our meals and refilling our water glasses. Plus, if I thought that God was the sum of my experiences, then I already knew him, her, them, it, anyway. I was working overtime to justify my desire to get out of this house. If leaving meant I could have some peace and make the questions stop once and for all, or if I could exist in this "happily ever after life" with the little bit of romance in which I still believed left intact, I didn't need to meet God. I didn't need to learn more about the true meaning of Fate.

The problem was that this wasn't exactly the kind of dinner party from which you excused yourself with a fake story about not feeling well. Presumably, our assumed host could literally see right through us. *I could see through myself.* No. I knew I wasn't going to leave until I was dismissed. I was in for the duration. And I was spiraling.

This spiraling feeling was not new. It always left me exhausted and depressed. But, again, in *heaven?* Shouldn't this be the place where I was finally freed from this internal conflict? Wasn't heaven supposed to be the reward for having suffered through life? Wasn't this the place where I should finally find peace and relief? I once read a book called *10% Happier.* The author, Dan Harris, wrote that he wanted the title to be, "The Voice in My Head is an Asshole." I was starting to think that maybe that voice was Fate.

I was in danger of a full-blown panic attack when I felt a hand on my shoulder. It was the kind of gentle, reassuring touch that said, "Dude, just take a deep breath and let the process unfold." I turned to thank Mort. Unaware of my meltdown, he was sitting with his hands pressed to his face in delight. He clearly loved every minute of this show. Even the part, especially the part, where Fate took credit for the car accident that first introduced him to Jeanie. I looked toward the shape at the end of the table, and unless my eyes were still playing games with me, it gave me a gentle nod. The kind of nod that said, "Just take a deep breath and let the process unfold." And then gently, "Trust yourself."

Trust who? Trust what? And then, silence in my head. I finally ran out of questions.

Fate had a mission, and it was bigger than me. Bigger than my endless stream of questions. Bigger than my insecurities. The show must go on. I suspected I wasn't the first person to feel some level of shock. Fate probably knew exactly how to deal with guests like me. I took a few deep breaths and came to grips with the truth.

If I were totally honest with myself, any disappointment I felt was owed to my inability to take advantage of the opportunities that Fate allegedly gave me. This disappointment and my reaction were on me. My fault. Not Fate's.

Fate was still talking as I regained consciousness of the moment. "—And so I invite all of you to clear any glasses, utensils, or napkins to the side and imagine your placemat is a screen."

I wondered what I had missed. It made me wonder about all the things I had missed when I was too busy asking myself too many questions.

I turned to Mort, who gave me a look that was a combination of compassion and curiosity. He shrugged with a big smile and turned his attention to his screen/placemat. I didn't get the impression that Mort ever asked too many questions. I think he was all in for whatever was in front of him. I'm guessing he lived his life like that, and I bet it had served him well. He had a plan, and he had faith. No sense stopping now. I had run out of questions and figured I'd give that strategy a try. For once. I was here. I may as well appreciate it, try on a little faith of my own, and see how it fits.

Still, I felt strange looking into a placemat. I was self-conscious even though everyone at the table was doing the same. I found myself stealing glances out of the tops and corners of my eyes. Kind of like I did when I took my first yoga class and felt totally out of place. Or maybe more to the point, when I was a kid in temple, spying on those around me who were praying. Even then, I was uncomfortable with the vulnerability of my faith. That's exactly how faith felt. Vulnerable. It required a sort of letting go that was simply foreign to me—even if I wanted it. It required me to give up control. I heard a different voice in my head this time. Mine. *Trust yourself.*

Fate continued. "This is a unique opportunity that you're all about to experience. When you were alive, did you ever wonder if those in heaven could see you? How many of you asked if your grandmother, spouse, son, or even dog could look down on you?"

That was a question everyone could relate to. We all raised our hands.

"Now that you're here, who would you like to see?"

There was a collective anticipation manifested by a single gasp. Playfully, Fate said, "Well? What are you waiting for?" Then Fate commanded, "Let there be no light!"

It was funny. I wondered if God was amused as Fate riffed on one of the all-time most famous lines. And I wondered how many times it had been delivered. I wondered if it got old, like a band playing its greatest hit night after night.

The room went dark, and a wave of thoughts raced through my mind like a slideshow. I had heard that some people literally see their lives flash before their eyes just before they die. I experienced something like that only in reverse. Sort of. Not exactly opposite, I guess. I saw my life, but I was already dead. I saw Timmy, Adam, Blondie, teachers, people, moments, the cars, and, of course, Jess. My expectation was that the placemat would show me how she was doing. I was so eager to see what Jess was cooking and hear what music she was listening to. I wanted to know, *I needed to know* that she was okay. Maybe she'd be sitting outside on one of our old, beat-up chairs sipping tea. Did she still live there? Maybe I'd see Tim. I could find out who he was dating. I wondered what kind of car he was driving now. Maybe I'd interrupt him mid-coitus. Is this a PG placemat? Oh! My boys at The Gym! Was my seat still there? I hoped they were all okay. I almost felt giddy. Any of these scenes would have been amazing.

I was shocked to see my mom and sister.

Maybe my placemat was broken. Do these things have bars on them to let the user know if the signal is strong enough? I looked over at Mort's placemat, and he whispered with tears streaming down his face, "It's Jeanie. My Jeanie." Everyone seemed to be seeing their most beloved. I was looking at my mom and sister. The two people from my life who I felt understood me the least.

I raised my hand and asked quietly and hesitantly, whispering, "Ummmm, is it Fate? Mr. Fate? Yes? Mr. Fate, I think there must be some mistake. Maybe a crossed signal? Does that happen with these placemats? Like phone lines getting crossed? I'm pretty sure that you're giving us the most incredible opportunity to reconnect with the hearts of our lives, and I'm not sure—"

Fate interrupted me by placing his finger up to his mask. The angels sang, "Shhhhhhhhhh . . ."

Wow. Did I just get shushed in heaven . . . by angels?

This death thing was not turning out the way I had expected. I felt that invisible hand on my shoulder again. If I were going to have this opportunity, I should, at the very least, see what it meant, right? Maybe it was a sign? Were there still signs in heaven? Oh wait. I was done with questions. I was supposed to be a new man. Fine.

My sister and mom both sat silently in the living room of the house where I lived until I left for college. This was the room I sprinted through during my escape to the backyard when I ran away as a kid. My mom was in the oversized red chair next to the fireplace, and my sister was on the white couch. The room hadn't been remodeled since the early 1980s, and every piece of furniture had a different floral pattern. My mom used to say that she loved this room because the patterns created a "botanical garden of furniture." Now the floral patterns were old and faded and no longer coordinated with one another. The garden was dead. The art on the walls was equally faded and straight out of earlier decades. The room would have been the ideal setting for a retro porn shoot. Now it was just a setting for two people unsure what to say to one another.

There was a time when my mom and I had gotten along. We were close. It was before my therapy unwound where I came from. Before

I understood how my parents' fights fucked me up. I always said that the hardest part of therapy is picking at the scars. Once you open up those things, it's hard to stop picking at them and even harder to stop the bleeding.

She would read to me in this room. We would play games in this room. All three of us. All five of us: my mom, dad, sister, me, and Blondie. We'd laugh and pretend not to notice the tightness in the air. The tension. We were, after all, a model family. We had an impression to maintain. But that's all I ever wanted. More than anything. Not the perfect family, but a close one. A family that could fight and love again. Or maybe even not fight. Just love. When my sister moved across the country, we tried to become close, but that was hard too. We just couldn't seem to get out of our own way. Looking into my placemat was making me sad. I was still picking at the scars.

Fate spoke with the kind of tone that a therapist or hypnotist might have. Calmly. Slowly. Monotone. "Keep watching your loved ones." He went on to explain what or who we were seeing. "I don't have anything to do with what appears before you. If your heart is free, you will see the person you love in the purest, deepest way."

That explained Mort and Jeanie. Before I could raise my hand, Fate continued. "But if your heart carries regret, that is what you will see." That hurt. Fate had just punched me in the gut.

I had a friend whose mom had died. We were hiking together, and I remember asking him if I would regret not repairing my relationship with my mom if she died before I did. He never hesitated. In fact, he stopped walking, grabbed my arm, and looked directly into my eyes in a way that was completely out of character. He wasn't fucking around.

"Yes," he told me. "Do whatever you have to do to figure out how to exist together in peace. Do not, under any circumstances, allow anything to be unresolved." He had never talked to me like that. I felt his pain.

I tried. I really thought I had tried. Each time I thought we had it worked out, we just slipped back into the same old patterns. Finally, I just gave up. It turns out I carried the regret with me through life and into death. It didn't matter if she died before me or I died before her. So now instead of experiencing Jess, I'm experiencing that regret. My friend was right. I felt like I was in prison expecting a conjugal visit, and my lawyer showed up instead. Still fucked. Just not in the good way.

I watched as my mom and sister put down their books and started talking to one another. They were talking about me. Remember when this . . . Remember when that . . . They talked about the time Jond and I snuck out of our rooms and hid under the eucalyptus tree. My mom talked about my series of sports injuries, especially my broken leg and concussions. My sister asked my mom if she knew what I was writing about. She asked how long it had been since my mom and I had talked. My mom didn't know the answer to either question. She started to cry.

"I lost him at some point. I tried," she told my sister. "I really thought I tried. Finally, I just gave up. Each time I thought we had it worked out, we just slipped back into the same old patterns. And now all I feel is regret."

I slowly looked up at Fate. He was prepared, waiting for my eyes. I meant to think it but said it out loud, "That's exactly what I just thought. Word for word. She feels the same way. Exactly the same way."

Fate slowly nodded. I started to wonder about the expression under the mask but wasn't going to add this question to the Encyclopedia of Questions or this moment to Erik's List of Missed Moments.

My sister got up from the couch, slowly walked to my mom, and knelt on the floor in front of that oversized red chair with the faded flowers. "You both did the best you could, you know. Erik needed someone to blame for whatever he felt like he was missing in his life."

I wanted to defend myself, but she was probably right. Maybe not entirely right, but mostly.

"He was nearly fifty years old, Mom. He had every chance to make a choice and just let it all go." They were both crying now.

"I wish that . . ." my mom wailed, unable to finish the thought. Then, my sister, God bless her, *really, I thought, please, God, bless her*, said the most amazing thing. "He knows, Mom. Erik can hear you right now, and he knows. No more regrets for either of you."

How did she? Wait, what? Oh, how I wanted to just ask a billion questions. As she said this to my mom, I swore she was looking at me. I felt a hand on my shoulder. This time it was Mort's.

"Don't you get it, Erik? She loves you. She always did." Then he added, "Forgive yourself."

Forgive myself? I wanted to defensively blurt out, "What the hell is that supposed to mean?" But he was right. I just hadn't ever thought of it that way. The anger I was holding onto had turned into blame and then shame. All of which made me treat them terribly. All of which made me feel guilty. All of which created a spiral from which I could never recover. This wasn't their fault anymore. I was a big boy, and after some time, it couldn't be their fault anymore. Not that it ever was. It was my choice to hang onto all that I held onto. My fault to keep stuffing my suitcase full of more and more shame. The longer I went without a relationship with them . . . the more I blamed myself. Mort was right. I had dug the hole I was in. I needed to forgive myself. But it was more than just that. I abandoned my childhood after that fight when I was seven. I abandoned myself. I needed to make peace with that, too. I quietly wished that I could see them again and make everything different.

I leaned back in my chair and took a deep, cleansing breath. Fate startled me as he cleared his throat with a kind of annoyed "Excuse me, dude, but I'm not done with you" tone. I opened my eyes, leaned forward, and shrugged my shoulders with a return look of "What do you mean you're not done with me?"

He cocked his head playfully and then said, "No, Ray. It was you."[8]

What? I knew the reference. Maybe it was time to warm up to this Fate character. Dude had a seriously warped sense of humor. He was quoting *Field of Dreams*. I just didn't understand why.

Then I got it. In the movie, Kevin Costner's character, Ray Kinsella, figures out that he had to let go of the guilt and anger he felt about his father to be happy. He had to let go of that burden. Granted, in the movie, Ray was alive, and his dad was dead. The exact opposite of what I was experiencing, but there was still great reward for giving in to peace. Ray got to play catch with his dad, and I got . . .

Jess.

There she was, sitting on the back deck of our little guesthouse. Just like I had hoped. The weathered wood was still badly in need of new stain and the same three slats remained dangerously missing. I was supposed to fix that. What I wouldn't give to be able to do it now. Jess wore an oversized shirt over her knees, which were pulled to her chest. Her long hair flowed from her favorite hemp hat that we bought at a music festival. She wasn't sure how it looked, but it was perfect on her. On brand. She sipped mint tea from the big mug with the tie-dyed design. We bought that on Haight Street in San Francisco. The shadows and breeze told me it was mid-afternoon. She looked peaceful. Daydreaming.

Then the placemat went dark. It was just a blink of a moment, but it was enough because I was wholly in it. Was this what faith felt like? Was faith less about religion or spirituality and really about awareness? Was having faith in yourself simply being aware of yourself? They seemed like okay questions to ask. For once, I was going to feel grateful for what I had and not focus on what I was missing.

CHAPTER THIRTEEN

An unhoused man approaches a businessman and asks for money
to buy a lottery ticket. Despite thinking it is just an excuse, the
businessman gives the down-on-his-luck traveler a few dollars.
The next day, the man is waiting for the Good Samaritan. He had
won and wanted to share the news . . . and the winnings.

The lights came back on, and a sense of calm settled around the table. A sense of peace. A sense of satisfaction. I had always feared and despised the idea of being content. It felt like I was giving up and settling. If I felt content, it meant I was no longer seeking to move forward. No longer searching for a challenge. No longer wanting to better myself. To me, content meant the death of ambition and drive. I was the living embodiment of an Alan Watts quote, ". . . everybody rushes around in a great panic as if it were necessary to achieve something beyond themselves."[9]

That was me. Looking beyond myself. Always panicked with a slow, low-burning anxiety. According to the therapists, this was the result of feeling like I was never enough. I always needed to do more. To be more. This is how I proved my value. For the first time in my life . . . *damn* . . . I mean for the first time ever, I felt like I didn't need to do that anymore.

I was doing it wrong. The real meaning of contentment was that you had peace in your heart. It was a result of authenticity. If you were at peace driving forward, you could be content. If you were authentic about your place in life, you could be content. Contentment wasn't weak. It was beautiful. Contentment wasn't a slow death. It was honest. I think that by taking responsibility for my role in the downward cycle of my relationship with my mom and sister, I felt more authentic, which allowed me, for the first time, to experience how contentment should feel: empowering.

I had an expectation that heaven was the place where questions automatically stopped. Where everything was forgiven and healed. The place where everything was perfect upon arrival. Where *I* was perfect upon arrival. That certainly wasn't my experience. Heaven, instead, appeared to be the place where I had the opportunity to safely free myself from all the fears that haunted me in life. A place where I could let go of the pain that I caused with lies and deceit. In life, I was always afraid of hurting people if I followed my soul. I couldn't be content. It felt selfish. "Me first" was never an option. In life, I privately feared that my actions would, if heaven existed, keep me from being welcomed. It's not that I thought there was a hell. Just that heaven was a kind of tennis and golf club to which you needed a special invitation to join.

Now I was thinking that everyone was welcomed if they were willing to allow themselves to be exposed and their true authenticity revealed. Frankly, after seeing my mom and sister, I stopped thinking of heaven as a location altogether. It was spiritual. Heaven was a feeling. Authentic contentment.

I thought about all the times when I described something unspeakably beautiful in nature as "heaven on earth." No. Heaven on earth was actually something in me. Heaven on earth was the beauty of a pure heart. With a pure heart, only then can we see true beauty in any other form, be it in nature, music, art, or humanity. Only then can we truly experience love.

I had moments in my life when I felt overwhelmed by the Colorado backcountry or the way Jess looked at me. Now I knew what those moments really were. They were moments when I was content. Pure belonging. Pure of heart. Pure peace. I struggled not to give in to the temptation and think about all that I missed because I hadn't understood it when I was alive. How much more life could I have experienced? How many more moments? How could I have loved myself?

Fate settled at the center of the table, his legs crossed atop something like a lazy Susan. He spun slowly, an enigmatic smile playing on his lips, his expression both serene and mysterious. My mom would have misidentified it as an "eating-shit grin" instead of what it really was—a "shit-eating grin." She had a funny habit of getting things slightly wrong. Like always calling the movie *Moneyball,* based on Michael Lewis' book and the Oakland A's, "Money Balls." I teased her that she made it sound like porn. In that version, the general manager probably wouldn't be named Billy Beane, as he was in the actual book. No. In the porn version, he'd be something like Billy Boner. Until this very moment, that habit of hers annoyed me to no end. Now I felt like I was going to miss it. *Billy Boner. That's funny.*

As Fate continued to spin with that clown-like grin, I felt wide open. Unlike any other time in my, well, any other time ever. I felt totally in the moment. What came before didn't matter. What happened next wasn't a consideration. I was a mixed cocktail of these powerful, positive emotions. As Fate kept spinning in silence, I finally noticed the boy sitting to my left. I had been so stuck in my own experience and so taken by Mort that until now, I hadn't even noticed this boy. I hadn't made any effort to introduce myself. As much as I always prided myself on being aware of the people and activities around me, I certainly didn't hold up to that standard here. Epic fail. I hadn't even noticed someone sitting right next to me. Much less a kid. How could I have missed him?

Trying to introduce myself, I leaned over, offered my hand, and whispered, "I'm Erik." He just stared straight ahead, transfixed, without any hint of emotion. Maybe he didn't speak English? It would be just like me to assume that he did. Or that he'd want to talk to me. Maybe he was just too scared. Or shy.

He was only about fifteen and wore the white Hurley T-shirt and tattered jeans that were the uniform of his generation. He wore blue

Vans, slip-ons, no laces. Total skater vibe with his shoulder-length brown highlighted hair covered by a backward sun-bleached, red baseball hat featuring a Minor League Baseball team logo. I guess he looked Hispanic. I wasn't sure. Maybe Native American?

His complexion was dark, but his origin wasn't the only feature that felt unclear to me. Something wasn't right. It felt like something was missing. Two eyes. Two ears. Nose. Everything physical seemed to be in order. But while everyone else in the room felt vibrant, this kid felt distant. Cold. Like his spirit wasn't in the room. Like he was there, but he wasn't there. Transparent.

Perhaps he was angry. I didn't know his story, but who could blame him for being pissed if he were here at such a young age? He violently pushed back his chair, sending it crashing to the floor behind us, and bolted out of the room as the lights came all the way up. I wanted badly to rush after him. Nobody else seemed to flinch when his chair exploded onto the floor. It created a huge crash. *How could they not notice something so totally out of place?* Amid peace and contentment was an almost violent level of emotion. *Where did he go?* These thoughts were interrupted.

Harry Caray was back. "Alllll riiiiiight!!! It's time for intermission. We hope you all enjoyed the first act. Please take a few minutes to walk around, introduce yourselves to some new friends, and, of course, join me in singing 'Take Me Out to the Ballgame'!"

This was our seventh-inning stretch.

He wasted no time diving into his signature song. "A-one, a-two, a-three! Take me out to the baaaaaall gaaaaaaammme . . ." We broke out in chorus with the angels filling in as the Universe's greatest backup singers. It didn't even faze me that everyone knew the words when I assumed at least half the people in the room had never heard the song, much less seen a baseball game. Asking that question would only take away the enjoyment of the moment. I was more than happy to sing along and nothing more. "For it's one, two, three strikes, you're out at the ollllllld ballllllll gaaaaaame!"

Harry finished up with another "Alllllll riiiiiight!" and invited us to head outside to enjoy what he called "the fireworks show." One by one, we all streamed outside through the sliding glass doors. I could swear that we walked through the same doors that previously led from the pool and the giant lawn where we played earlier. They, um, were gone. No pool. No field. I just smiled and laughed. *Of course they're gone.* In their place was an amphitheater with hundreds of oversized, plush seats that were angled slightly to give the perfect view of the pitch-black sky above us.

I sank into a soft, bean-bag-like cushion next to Mort, leaned back, and looked up into the blackness. I was expecting a familiar show and waited for the first firework to burst into the sky. Usually, it was a small one. Something to just whet the audience's appetite. One of those traditional rockets that screams into the night and booms into a sprinkling flower of color.

Apparently, I was a slow learner. Why I still expected the same thing I had experienced in life was beyond me. Why did I expect anything? What was the point? This was to be a fireworks show like no other.

I was surprised by a shooting star that streaked across the canvas of night. First just the one. Then a second. And a third. One by one, these stars shot across the sky, each creating a unique pattern of light in their wake. As though each was its own paintbrush. Their patterns were like clouds, and my eyes could make out shapes in the light.

A horse.

Or a dog.

A little girl.

A unicorn.

There's a lobster.

Hundreds of shapes. One at a time. Was this the fireworks show? I wasn't complaining, but . . . then the sky exploded! A huge parade of shooting stars lit up the sky, creating intricate patterns that were less like individual shapes and more like master canvases. Seeing them this close, speeding across the sky just above our heads was . . . it was . . .

I don't have the words. Unimaginable? Indescribable? Unfathomable? None of those explain what was happening above us. Or how I felt.

Wait. Transformative. Even if I hadn't just sat at a table with who I thought was God, it would be impossible to deny this existence or universal energy. Maybe these shooting stars were just part of the universe, something explainable as a natural happening at the intersection of time and environment. Something explained away by science that happened because of a provable equation. But in this moment, I chose to believe in something bigger. I closed my eyes and whispered, "Thank you." A prayer. Was this faith?

When I opened my eyes, I gazed around at others in their chairs as the show continued. An old habit. I always liked watching the reactions of others. It didn't matter if I was at a movie, baseball game, or holiday parade, I would try to figure out what people were thinking or experiencing.

Is the boy here? Where is the boy?

There! A few rows below me and a few seats to my right sat the boy with the faded Minor League Baseball hat. The logo was turned toward me. I couldn't see his face. I had no idea how he was reacting. But as people instinctively hooted and hollered, pointed, and shrieked, he seemed to sit completely still. No gestures. Totally motionless. *Maybe he's blind. Is that why he isn't reacting to the fireworks? Is that why he didn't respond to my attempts to introduce myself earlier? Yeah, idiot, because not being able to see would affect his ability to hear you.* I could still be a total dick, apparently.

In between starbursts, I asked Mort what he thought about the boy's lack of response.

"We all have our own experiences, Erik. Don't try to interpret his through your eyes."

I got defensive. I tried to protest and explain that I wasn't suggesting that he was doing something wrong. Just the opposite. I was convinced that there was something bigger going on with that kid. He just didn't seem right. I explained to Mort that I wanted to help him, not judge or blame him.

Mort still wasn't having it. "If he needs help, he'll ask you for it," he said with a stern and completely confident it's-not-about-you tone, as though he was telling me to back off.

Okay, dude, fine. I get it.

As the stars continued to race across the sky, I couldn't take my eyes off the kid. *What was it about this damn kid?* I wanted to get up from the universe's most comfortable chair and get closer.

In my focus on the boy, I hadn't noticed that Fate was now standing in front of this theater. Was he now going to lecture us? Was he going to make a presentation? I looked around to see if God was outside with us, but I didn't see him. The stars had stopped shooting.

Fate spoke. "I want to show you something."

CHAPTER FOURTEEN

On her first day, a new nurse cares for a premature baby. Twenty-eight years later, and after having moved across the country, the nurse is caring for another baby. The mother was the original baby.[10]

Fate introduced the start of a movie, and after the opening credits and titles, we saw a young girl walking down a sunlit, deserted street in what appeared to be a pretty rough neighborhood. Graffiti covered the outer walls of houses. Thick, black bars protected the doors and windows. Cars were parked on the sidewalks. Some were up on blocks. Weeds were landscaping. The girl was in her early teens, and she had a spring in her step that didn't quite fit with the scenery. She wore a hoodie and jeans and was listening to music through headphones. She sang along to old Eminem lyrics. *Does anybody else know they are Eminem lyrics?*

Fate paused the movie. "Do you know the story of Thurgood Marshall?" No response, which was either the result of confused silence or none of us knowing. "He was a United States Supreme Court Justice and civil rights leader. When Thurgood was fourteen, as he walked through his neighborhood, he found a law book in the street. The book had no business being there. It was completely out of place. Thurgood picked it up, started reading, and, well, the rest, as they say . . ."

I thought that was an unbelievably cool story. What were the chances? How did that book get there? Without thinking about my surroundings or the last several hours of my experiences, again, I was going to say it was one of the coolest experiences of my "life." But this wasn't life. Not anymore.

I love it when things like that happen. The words were barely in my head when the light bulb went off. Fate put that book there! Just like Fate put Jeanie in Mort's way. Why did I think finding that book was so awesome but was upset that Mort's story had "changed"? Maybe I felt like this removed some of the randomness of a lifelong romance. It wasn't just by chance. It was, in fact, fated. Like being punked, but better. I was getting a better grip and thought that both instances of Fate's power were undeniably cool. He was God's court jester. Not to make fun of people. Not to make fools of people. But to help them. Mort needed Jeanie, and Fate made it happen. This satisfied God.

Behind his mask, I can only assume Fate was laughing at me and thinking, "Of course that's what I did, dumbass. Haven't I made that abundantly clear by now?"

Fate explained, "This girl is not much younger than Thurgood was when he found his law book. And it seems to me that this girl could possibly use a nudge in a new direction. In front of you is a keypad with three buttons. If you push A, she will find a book like the one Thurgood found. If you push B, she will find a biography of Wilma Rudolph, and if you push C, she will find a biography of Nina Simone."

We looked around, trying to read each other with our eyes as if to ask, "A? Are you picking A? I'm thinking C. Don't pick A." Was Fate really leaving this kid's, um, fate, up to us? Were we really going to have this kind of potential impact on this kid? Could we really help dictate her future? It was exciting to think about. I was trying not to judge this kid's life, but if I were being honest with myself, it didn't look like the choices offered much in the way of hope.

Lawyer and activist?

Great athlete?

Musical artist?

What did I want for this girl I knew nothing about? At one time or another in my life, I wanted all of these things for myself. Well, maybe not a lawyer. Who wants to be a lawyer? Taking on anything that required extra school wasn't exactly in my wheelhouse. But pro athlete or artist? Those were the dreams of my childhood and adulthood. Especially artist. That one was still my dream. Right up until the end, I harbored those not-so-secret dreams of writing for a living. Or just creating for a living. Anything. I wanted to leave something behind. Not a legacy. I didn't care about that, but art that stood the test of time.

I pushed the button for C and prayed for everyone else to do the same. I had always wanted that for myself, and I had also long thought that if I ever had a kid of my own, that's what I would want for them. An openly creative life that gave them the opportunity to explore and express feelings through words, mixed media, or music. Or through any other kind of art, for that matter. Once, while applying for a job, the hiring manager said to me, "You're really kind of an artist, aren't you?" It was the single greatest compliment I had ever received—even if it meant not getting the job since he saw my artistic spirit as a weakness and not an asset. The artist's life seemed to be full of feeling. Pure of heart. Contentment. Awareness. Full of heaven on earth. Even in its struggles. Authenticity through art was worth the struggle. Worth the pain.

So, yeah, I pushed C.

Fate was back to his playful ways. "I'll go tally the votes," he said.

I figured the votes were probably tallied automatically, but he wanted to create some drama. Kind of like cutting to commercial at a crucial moment. This was his cliffhanger. As he stepped away, the angels broke into the "Final Jeopardy" theme music. *Of course, they did.* When Fate came back, he didn't announce the winner. He just said, "Watch."

The girl continued her carefree stroll down the street, rapping platinum-worthy lyrics about drugs, guns, more drugs, and . . . drugs. Lo and behold, she tripped over a book. It was, not surprisingly, completely out of place. She picked it up and started flipping through the pages. We couldn't see which book it was. We couldn't see what she was reading. We had no idea if it was the law book or the Nina Simone biography. We were all on the literal edge of our seats. Even Blondie, who found her way onto the seat next to me where Mort once sat. *What happened to Mort?* We were yelling and barking at the screen as though it were the *Rocky Horror Picture Show.* Obviously, not everyone was hoping for C. According to the hoots and hollers, this vote was going to be close, but most seemed to want her to become a lawyer. Probably because of the stability and . . . *oh, shut up already.*

I thought about all of the years when I would answer anyone who would ask, "What do you want to do with your life?" with "I want to be a writer. If I could make a living doing anything, I would write." But I tied "the living" to money. If only I had figured out that the earned living came from the doing—not the money. Earning a living isn't about the earning. It's about the living.

Then I'd go back to my life of shoulds and supposed-tos. I'd go back to my life of perceived responsibilities. Responsibilities, I convinced myself, required so many sacrifices and compromises that they became excuses for not writing. My life where risk wasn't sweetened by reward, as Thoreau wrote, but instead was met by doubters and naysayers. The life in which I didn't have the strength to realize that it wasn't a risk to write for a living; the real risk was not writing.

I used to think of "risking my life" as something that involved death. I was wrong. I only now truly understood that I was risking my life by not fully living it. According to my terms. Every day that I wasn't a writer or an artist, every day when I didn't say what I needed to say, every day that wasn't driven by love, passion, and gratitude was a day that I risked my life. It was a day when I was already dead. Just like Ira said. I may have appeared to be alive on the outside, but I was dead on the inside. I figured this all out on the day I died. That day was filled with love, passion, and creativity. That day was filled with a run on the mountain, making love to Jess, and writing in my hidden café. I was fulfilled. I was alive. I didn't earn a dime. I earned something far more valuable: I earned my self-respect. I earned a living.

Oh, how I wanted this kid to learn this lesson early and to be an artist. She had a great voice. Maybe she'd be a rapper herself. Even though the book was already in her hand, I kept pushing C the way a little kid keeps pushing a crosswalk signal. Maybe if I just pushed it a few more times . . .

The girl closed the book, leaned back on the hood of a broken-down car, and looked up at the sky. Was she looking at us? Did she know that we had just delivered her the choice of a new path? Was she visualizing her music career? She closed her eyes. Was she praying? What was she thinking? I wished Fate or God would translate the moment for us. I was desperate to know which book was in her hand.

"You've just participated in a powerful event," Fate broke the tension with the return of the monotone delivery. It was right for the perceived reverence of the moment. Still, someone yelled, "Which book is it?" Fate looked in the direction of the would-be heckler and said with complete sincerity, "It doesn't matter."

This caused immediate confusion, disappointed groans, and a few "What do you mean, it doesn't matter?" responses from the crowd.

I understood exactly what he meant. We all made our A, B, or C selections based on some personal and even unconscious bias. I wanted her to receive a book on artistry because I wanted her to have a path I had missed. A path I respected. A path that I didn't honor in my life. In some way, I wanted to live vicariously through this kid. But my path might not have been the right path for her. Fate knew more about this kid than we did. I started to think that the joke, again, was on us. It dawned on me that we didn't really pick the book the kid found. It occurred to me that Thurgood Marshall probably never even found a book in the street. This was just another exercise to get us to think about our truth. Our core. Fate was going to pick the book all along. He just let us feel as though we had something to do with it. There was a chance that the whole scene was faked. Maybe Fate was also the sum of my experiences viewed through a different lens. *Holy shit, was I Fate, too?* Was Fate also made in my image, just as I had considered God? He looked right at me as I thought through this possibility, and he nodded ever so slightly. *Mad respect, Fate. Mad respect.*

"Want to vote some more?" he asked excitedly in his animated way. Of course, they all did. I'm not sure if anyone else had figured out that they had nothing to do with the actual outcomes, but they were thrilled to continue. Maybe I needed to give them more credit. Maybe they all knew just like I did, and it was like watching professional wrestling. It wasn't real, but you couldn't stop watching. I wanted to watch more. I wanted to vote more. If for no other reason than to get a deeper glimpse into my own truth. I wanted to learn more about my truth and biases.

But first, I really had to pee.

I wasn't sure if I was allowed to get up, but this was one of those "even-though-the-fasten-seatbelt-sign-is-on-I-have-to-get-up" kind of moments. If you ask, the flight attendants won't tell you it's okay, but it's clear they'd rather you get up now than clean up later.

As I left my seat, I had a flashback to my college days of walking out of lectures halfway through class. It always made me anxious and nervous. Like I was breaking some rule, or worse, disrespecting the professor. Blondie jumped down from her chair without a hint of anxiety, and we walked to the top of the amphitheater stairs.

When we got to the last step, the house was gone. In its place, we found a long, dirt path that framed the top row of seats and continued into darkness beyond either side of the theater. There were no signs pointing to any restrooms. At this point, following the path into the darkness was a no-brainer. It had to lead somewhere. I was so afraid to follow paths like this in life—be it metaphorically or literally—might as well have a go at it now. I looked at Blondie, and with a shrug of my shoulders, we went right.

I had always described my bouts of sadness—okay, let's call a spade a spade: my depression—as "going dark." I described the feelings as skipping along without a care in the world and then falling into a deep well without a hint of warning. As though someone left a manhole cover off. I liked to pretend that I didn't know why it happened. But for me, it wasn't a chemical problem. It was an authenticity problem. I wasn't living whole, and the further I got from living whole, the further I ran from contentment, the darker I became. Still, I pretended that

I didn't know why it happened. Timmy used to mock me for that. "Right, Shirl, you have no idea why. Shut the fuck up." He was the king of tough love. The thing is, I knew I had an authenticity problem. I just didn't know why.

I wrote a suicide note once. Twenty pages. It was maybe the single best thing I ever actually wrote because it was the most honest. I always gave it to my therapists to read. It didn't matter if they read it the day after I wrote it or fifteen years later; I was still stuck in the same place. In the same fear. In the same cycle. The more I ignored it, the more I sabotaged myself. And the more I did that, the longer the past became. The longer the past got, the more I struggled to overcome, and the darker life felt. It wasn't hard to figure out.

This path felt like it had the makings of falling through a hole into the darkness I used to experience. But I wasn't scared. Walking this path into the unknown was completely invigorating. "Where are we going, Blondie? Where's the damn bathroom?!" *Wait. Strange.* I didn't even feel like I had to go anymore. *Why would someone need to pee in heaven anyway?*

I could still hear Fate's movie presentation in the background. The same way I used to hear a band playing its encore when I was already in the parking lot to beat the traffic. It was a dull echo punctuated by the roar of the crowd. My eyes were adjusting to the darkness, and I saw a weird light up ahead. It wasn't a point of light, like a bulb. It looked like a long, thin line. Then, two thin lines that created an L shape. I couldn't figure out what it was. I couldn't figure out how far away it was. I wondered if Blondie saw it.

As we got closer, the "L" grew bigger and became something like a U and then a rectangle. Before long, we were standing in front of a door. The light on the inside created the glowing rectangle through the cracks in the frame. I knocked and waited, but nobody answered. Blindly, I slid my hand around, looking for a doorknob, but found nothing. How would we get in? Because she's smarter than I am, Blondie simply nosed the door open.

The boy.

The boy I was sitting next to at dinner and the one who bolted out of the dining room and sat unmoved by the fireworks show. That boy now sat just as still at a desk, staring into a mirror.

I tried again. "Oh, hey. Sorry. Didn't know that anyone was in here. I'm Erik. We sat next to each—" This time, he turned to look at me. It was the first time he acknowledged my presence. I was forty-nine. He was maybe fifteen. Not going to lie, the kid's stare scared the shit out of me. His eyes were vacant. I continued to stand in the doorway. Blondie let out a little whimper, a cry, walked into the room, and curled up at his feet. Why did she do that? He kept staring at me. Through me.

"Did you like the fireworks show?"

Nothing.

"What did you have for dinner? My ribs were pretty good."

Nothing.

"Do you—did you have a dog? She seems to like you."

Nothing.

"Her name is Blondie."

Nothing.

"Did you stick around for the movie?"

Nothing.

"How did you vote?"

Nothing.

This kid was a fucking tough audience. I felt unnerved. What was the point of turning around and looking at me if he had nothing to say? His expression was just so . . . blank. Completely blank. I was feeling judged. I was feeling defensive. I finally couldn't take it anymore and made a complete ass out of myself. Slowly, I said, "DO. YOU. SPEAK. ENGLISH?"

Fuck. Did I really just do that? What a dick. It was so easy to fall into that old pattern. I felt defensive. I made it about me, and I went on the attack. *Idiot.* I was so disappointed in myself. Just as I was about to apologize, Blondie's ears perked up, and I heard a noise behind me.

Someone had cleared their throat. I jumped and turned to see what was going on and . . .

Oh. My. God.

The boy wasn't looking at me. He wasn't looking through me. He was looking past me.

"You're not supposed to be here," said Fate, flanked by two angels with black wings.

I had never seen black wings on angels. I didn't know there were black wings. *What the fuck is up with the black wings?*

I tried desperately to come up with an excuse, any excuse, for why I was in this random room with this random, mute kid and my dog. I tried the standard clichéd movie excuse for being in the wrong room. "I was looking for the men's room."

Fate wasn't having it. Black-winged angels apparently didn't have the necessary facial muscles to smile or laugh.

"Sorry. I'll just head back to the amphitheater. My bad. Let's go, Blondie."

Fate and his hench angels intervened. "It's not quite that simple now. You're going to need to come with us."

Seriously? Was I in a mafia movie? Was James Gandolfini here? I felt like I must be on *Candid Camera: Heaven*. I tried to keep joking. "Where to? Principal's office?"

Again. Not so amused.

Fate closed the door, and we disappeared back into the darkness. My heart tried desperately to leap out of my chest via my throat. I fought the urge to completely freak out and fall back into Question Land. Despite my best efforts, I couldn't keep one out of my mind: *Am I getting kicked out of heaven?* Okay, two. I couldn't keep two out of my mind: *Am I going to hell?*

CHAPTER FIFTEEN

The most famous member of the Atlanta Braves and Hall of Famer, Henry Aaron, passed away during the 2021 Major League Baseball season. The Braves won the World Series. They won forty-four games before the All-Star Break and forty-four games after. They won during the forty-fourth week of the year. Henry Aaron wore number 44.[11]

I'm fucked. For as long as I've been capable of thoughts, being alone with them was unsettling. But being alone with them and also . . . walking in a dark hallway . . . flanked by two black-winged angels . . . behind Fate . . . took that unsettled feeling to an entirely new level. *Fuuuuucked.* As we walked, I thought of all the times I offhandedly justified my actions with a laugh, "Well, you know, I'm already going to hell." Now I wondered if that was true. I never believed in hell, so this couldn't be possible, could it? This couldn't be my . . . fate? I was told for years, decades, that our thoughts dictated our realities. And if we changed our thoughts, we'd change our realities. I struggled with the execution of that, but I really hoped it was true at this moment. I didn't believe in hell. So, it couldn't exist, right? Right?

I was desperately fighting not to make up the kind of stories in my head that drove me to the edge of insanity during my life. I kept telling myself that none of the thoughts I was having were real, just as I had practiced after reading meditation books.

The truth was, however, that I didn't live the purest, kindest life. I left plenty of pain and broken hearts in my wake. I truly believed that I was a good person. I believed my intentions were almost always good. I had just failed to back them up consistently with my actions. I lied, and I cheated. I stole, and I coveted. Frankly, except for "Thou shalt not kill," none of the commandments were safe with me. What hurt most was that the commandments I most often broke were my own. No excuses, but not living authentically and in the direction of your soul results in the kind of actions you regret. Regardless of intention.

The heart I disrespected the most was my own. I cheated myself more than anybody else. Of personal truth and passion. I stole time from myself. I coveted a life that was disingenuous. I lived a life that was not representative of who I really was. Maybe I did kill. I just killed possibilities instead of people. In that divide between who I really was and the life I really lived, I hurt people. Some repeatedly. I was so afraid. If I ever did find my way into flow and clean living, I sabotaged it. I didn't think I deserved it. I felt full of shame for being happy.

I offered no excuses for myself or my actions, but there's that old cliché: "This is going to hurt me more than it hurts you." I hesitated to appear to be justifying anything, but that cliché might very well apply to me. Those I hurt seemed to move on. I never did. I carried the pain and personal disappointment with me. Always. I let it define me. If I made a mistake or hurt somebody, if I lied, stole, cheated, or didn't follow through on some goal, I'd beat myself up, refuse to forgive myself, and then pack it all into a bag that was always within arm's reach. No matter how stuffed and over-packed that bag got, I could always find a way to stuff in more disappointment and self-loathing.

Who was that guy who was sentenced to push the boulder up the hill only to have it roll back down? Sisyphus? I was like that guy. I should have had that guy tattooed on my calf. Only instead of pushing a boulder, I sentenced myself to life in prison without the possibility of parole. No double jeopardy rules for me. I re-tried myself and re-sentenced myself for the same crimes against humanity. Despite my personal breakthroughs and new understanding of contentment and risk, I still felt every ounce of my mistakes as we walked down the hallway. Call me Erikus.

Fate and the black-winged angels led Blondie and me into another room set up exactly like the one where I found the boy. White. Sparsely furnished with a twin bed, desk, chair, and mirror. A waiting room? Purgatory? I sat on the bed, and Blondie jumped up next to me. Fate took the seat at the desk. The black-winged angels stood guard at the door.

I tried to stall and keep it light. "Seems like God needs a better interior decorator." That got me nowhere. "So where's everyone else if you're here with me?"

Fate was still wearing his mask, which gave no indication of his mood or expression. He responded with, "You don't have to worry about them. They're fine."

I always hated the word "fine." It was such a bland expression, devoid of any kind of emotion. Vanilla. Not good. Not bad. Just "meh."

It was happening, however, and Fate's tone made me feel like I was in deep shit. He seemed kind of pissed off and stressed, and I worked hard not to add context that wasn't there. I reminded myself that I was the one who thought he was pissed and stressed. He had never said that.

Don't have a conversation that doesn't exist.

Don't have a conversation that doesn't exist.

Don't have a conversation that doesn't exist.

I was writing it over and over on a mental chalkboard.

"Listen, you weren't supposed to be in that room," Fate sighed, cutting to the chase. "You weren't supposed to see that boy."

I was immediately defensive. "I wanted to help him. There's something about him that just doesn't feel right." I started talking without taking a breath, offering an avalanche of justifications. "I had the best of intentions." I was telling the truth. "I didn't mean any harm. I got up with Blondie because I felt like you and I had a moment when I figured out the thing, and I really had to pee. And then . . ." I could not stop talking. ". . . I started walking down this hallway, which was super dark and normally would have freaked me out, but I just kept walking, and I felt so brave and bold, and I . . ." Blurting out one fast sentence after another. Rapid fire. I would have gone on forever if Fate hadn't rescued me from myself.

"Stop. Take a breath," Fate finally said.

I did exactly that. And then proceeded to hold it.

Fate laughed at me. "Seriously, Erik. Relax. You weren't supposed to be there, but you also didn't do anything wrong. You're not in any kind of trouble."

I let out a sigh of relief.

"Would it have killed you to lead with that?" This wasn't the time to play up the drama. I think if I had been standing, my knees would have buckled.

He continued. "If anything, we should apologize to you. We put you in a bad situation, and that's never our intention."

Whoa. That was my line. If ever there was a time when I wanted to sit in the moment, it was this one. Did Fate just cop to making a mistake? He mentioned "we." Was he suggesting that God made a mistake? I took another of those deep breaths and, with all the courage I could muster, asked, "What do you mean? What mistake? Who is 'we'?"

"You weren't supposed to see that boy. He wasn't even supposed to be at dinner." I wondered if that's why I hadn't seen him initially. Maybe he wasn't even there! I felt a momentary sense of entitlement. I wasn't in trouble, and, as a bonus, it turned out that I might not have lacked human awareness after all. Even still, I didn't totally understand. "So he snuck in or something?"

Fate took a deep breath of his own and started to explain. The boy had an accident. He and his friends routinely bombed their bikes down a steep hill and off a jump at the bottom. "They got tons of air," explained Fate. "Pretty impressive."

However, it was dangerous. The bottom of this hill intersected at a blind corner. If a car was coming, the jumper wouldn't be able to see it. A friend always stood watch to warn the jumper of cars, call "all clear!" and, if necessary, stop any cars if an attempt were already in progress.

The friends had a pact never to jump without each other. They swore on their lives.

The boy, it turned out, couldn't help himself and decided to try the jump without his friends around. On his fourth run down the hill, he hit the jump more perfectly than he ever had, and as he was flying, a car came around the corner. The windshield shattered on impact, and he went flying over the roof of the SUV, landing on his shoulder and head. His bike was destroyed. His helmet cracked in multiple places. Multiple bones were broken. Fate described the sounds of the crash in a grizzly detail that I didn't need. The sounds of tires screeching, glass shattering, and the collision created the worst kind of harmony that echoed through the boy's quiet, suburban street. Neighbors immediately came running from all directions. The boy's friends had to be held back by their parents as the ambulance drove him away.

I still didn't understand. *What am I doing here?*

"I need you to go back into that room. I'll finish explaining everything on the way."

Why did he bring me into this room in the first place just to have me go back?

I got up from the bed and called for Blondie. She wasn't too happy about being disturbed. She let out one of those displeased dog moans. She had found a perfect spot on the pillows. I always said that Blondie loved a good pillow. *Sorry, sweet girl, but this is one of those times when I really need you with me.* She forgave me quickly. Dogs are always far better at that than humans.

The black-winged angels moved away from the door and back into the hallway we went. It was no longer dark. I had never seen the Northern Lights except in pictures, but that's what the hallway looked like. Or the Space Mountain ride at Disneyland. Suffice to say, the hallway was far less daunting. Still, the beauty of the lights did little to assuage my anxiety about and sadness for the boy. To die so young. Why didn't he just go ask one of his friends to come out and stand point? What was he trying to prove? And to whom? What sort of pain was he hiding?

The hallway felt much longer when we walked it previously in the darkness. In the light, I could see we were less than one hundred feet from the original room. Fate stopped me just outside the door. "I know how you felt about the girl in the movie. You wanted her to enjoy the creative life you think you never experienced. You were always like that. More focus on what you didn't have than celebrating and honoring what was right in front of you."

I didn't understand what peeling back a few layers of my psychological onion had to do with this boy.

Fate said, "I need you to talk to him again."

Wait. What? "I've tried to talk to him. You know that. You watched me try to talk to him. He just looks through me. What, exactly, am I talking to him about?"

Fate took another deep, maybe slightly frustrated breath and shocked me with the punchline: "He can go back." And, after a beat, "He needs to go back."

"Go back where? You mean, *go back*, go back?" I was freaking out. HE CAN GO BACK? I didn't understand. "How can he go back? If he's here, he's dead. His friends and family are mourning. He . . ."

"No. That's what you picked up on and feel is missing. His spirit isn't here. He's somewhere between the hospital and here. He wasn't supposed to leave the hospital. It wasn't his time. He's halfway. He can't stay here. You picked up on it. That means he can hear you."

"Whoa. Isn't this God-level stuff? Who lives, who dies, and, I guess, who goes back? I don't know if you've noticed, but I'm not any kind of God."

Fate didn't argue with me. He went on to tell me that I had a chance to help this boy.

"Why me?"

"Because you need to do this."

He was right, I think. Even as I was forgiving myself. Even as I was learning to let go, I was still holding on to . . . something.

I opened the door slowly and stood just outside the threshold. I nervously looked at Fate, and he gave me one of those "go on" flicks of his wrists and fingers. You know the one. It's like International Sign Language for "What the hell are you so afraid of?"

"Hey, kid, it's me again. Third time's a charm and all, right?" I just started talking. I told him about my friend Steve, who lived in my neighborhood. Steve got hit by a car while riding a Big Wheel down the sidewalk. He was badly hurt but was now a firefighter saving other people's lives. I quietly wondered if that had been Fate's work too. I told the boy about my love of watching cars and tried to get him to laugh about the irony of being hit by one. He didn't laugh. He didn't do much of anything.

I told him about the girl in the movie and how I had pressed C. I told him about my parents' fights. I told him about Blondie, who was resting her head on his foot. I explained how funny Fate was. I tried to ask him questions about his friends. I told him about mine. "You'd love Timmy," I said. "In fact, you should go look him up." I asked him about sports and positions he played. I wondered who his favorite skater was and asked if he surfed. I was a rambling mess. Babbling run-on sentences. I was feeling desperate. He just stared.

I took a deep breath and stopped beating around the bush. "Listen, I want you to go back. I need you to go back. If you won't do it for you, do it for me. I messed up so many things in my life. I messed up love. I messed up passion. I messed up the meaning of risk and contentment. I messed up gratitude. I focused on the wrong things for so, so long, and I let fear dictate my days. My life. I didn't listen to Fate. I didn't listen to myself. You can do all of that. But only if you go back." I told him about Jess. I told him that he could learn from my mistakes. I could help him live a life of—

I stopped myself. Why would he care about going back for me? He didn't know me. What right did I have to tell him what to do? He was a teenager, after all. He didn't want to listen to some old dude. What was I missing?

I continued. "I know it sounds like I'm carrying tons of regret. I'm not. I'm trying not to. Not anymore. I now know that I did the best I could at the time. That's what we all do. That's all we can do. I'm guessing that you're scared. You're probably afraid that your friends are going to be mad and your parents are going to ground you. I know you swore on your life not to jump without a friend to stand watch, and you probably feel guilty. I promise that none of that matters. None of that is true. They just want you to be back with them. You're not going to be in trouble. You don't need to feel guilty or to carry any of this with you. They just want you back."

At some point, he had turned away from me and began looking at the wall, but now he turned and looked at me. That's what it was. He was afraid that he was going to be in trouble. He was afraid that his parents wouldn't love him. That his friends wouldn't talk to him. He had broken his promise to them. He felt ashamed. He needed permission to go back. To go be himself.

I walked to him, gave him a hug, and whispered in his ear. Privately. It was as honest a moment as I'd ever had in my life. Maybe only second to the time I cried after making love to Jess. But he needed to know. "Guilt is not worth dying over. Fear is not worth dying over. There is no shame. You have a lifetime of love and friendship ahead of you. You have a lifetime of memories to make. Go back."

He smiled. Still, he didn't talk. I really wanted him to talk.

I looked away from him and to the door to see if Fate was watching. When I turned back to talk to the boy some more, he was gone.

"Where did he go? Wheredidhego?" I panicked and stood up, frantically looking around the room.

"Back," Fate said with a single black tear rolling down his mask. "He went back."

CHAPTER SIXTEEN

An unemployed data analyst rides home on the train in London after another failed job interview. Unable to contain his emotions, he shares his entire story with the man sitting next to him. When they get off the train at the same stop, the man, a hiring manager for a tech company, offers him a better job than the ones he had been applying for.

The boy was gone.

Back to his family and friends.

Back to his life.

I sat quietly and thought about the opportunity he now had. How many times had I said, "If I only knew then what I know now"? The boy, perhaps, had learned the ultimate version of this cliché. Imagine the opportunity to learn from death and bring those lessons back to life. I wondered if he would remember our conversation. Would he be able to share his near-death experience with his family? *Or was it a death-death experience?* I had read a few books written by those who had such experiences. They described weird sounds, angels, voices, inner peace, deeper consciousness, and awareness. The book I'd really like to read is *Near Death: Ten Years Later.* I want to know if the lessons stuck. It's easy to find perspective. Much harder to keep it.

Still, I was always a little jealous of these experiences. It's warped, but I thought the people who had these experiences were "lucky."

In theory, I thought the perspective of nearly dying was the advantage of a lifetime. To get that second chance. But then, I had a few harrowing experiences of my own while backpacking in deep snow in the Colorado backcountry. Or the time I helped crew a world record attempt to swim the Sea of Cortez and got stuck in the middle of a huge tropical storm. We all thought we were going to die that night. Instead of coming back with renewed life, however, I merely tried to downplay the danger. "It wasn't that big of a deal." I guess it's not as much about the experience as it is about the person who had the experience. Even with something like my near-near-near-death experience, we need to be able to change. We need to allow the fear we feel or felt to mix with the perspective gained to create fearlessness. We need to integrate new learning into the old systems.

Maybe the boy would someday write his own book. His friends would, no doubt, love to hear stories of black-winged angels! I wondered if I would be remembered and, if so, how I would be described. Probably as just some ancient dude who was older than his parents. Or maybe he wouldn't remember anything at all.

Hopefully, the messages learned would be woven into the fabric of his soul. Maybe he would "just have a strange feeling" when presented with those life moments that challenged him to choose between fitting in or belonging. He wouldn't know why, but somehow, he'd always make the most self-expressive and self-loving choices. My hope was simply that, before death came, he would learn the most important lessons about life.

My God, how I wanted to talk to Jess. I wanted to tell her everything that had happened. I wanted to tell her about the boy. She had listened to me cry about my relationships with my mom and sister. She had dealt with my mood swings, darkness, and depression—the demons I fought daily. She tried to help with her words, actions, and love. But I struggled to accept any of it. These battles and the darkness were part of who I was, and as much as I hated them for making me feel weak and less than, I let them offer me a kind of security. Going dark was an excuse. I wished that I could have better used my demons to drive my writing or channel some kind of art; instead, I allowed them to suppress it. I allowed the demons to suppress me. Suppress who I really was. I allowed them to pick out my mask each morning—my reflection dictating who I pretended to be that day. Even at the very end, when things were better, I was still afraid to seize a day without some kind of mask. Without my security blanket.

Now, with the boy gone, as I sat on the bed and looked at the mirror above the desk, I only saw myself looking back. My own reflection. I flashed back to sitting on my bed with the bottle of pills when I was thirteen. The demons weren't gone, but I no longer had to fight them. If I had only just accepted them and realized that they were part of me. Because that is my truth. They are part of my authentic self. Fighting them meant not being authentic. Not being authentic meant feeling less than whole. Not feeling whole meant trying to fit in and looking for validation outside of myself. Not getting that validation . . . What a vicious cycle. No wonder the bottom dropped out repeatedly. Just over and over and over and over again.

I smiled in the mirror. And the reflection smiled back. I don't remember the last time that had happened. I wanted to tell Jess about all of this. I wanted to thank her. And apologize. She'd brush off the apology with some kind of "You're entitled to your experience" line, but I knew, secretly, she would appreciate it.

I looked at Blondie, again curled up on a pillow. She never questioned anything. She could sleep anywhere. Her mind didn't race. Her life was always about the moment. Perhaps that's why dogs were always so therapeutic. We have no choice but to be in their moment as we pet them. This time, I wouldn't wake her. I had faith that she would find me. Wherever I was.

I quietly got up from the bed and slipped out of the room. I wanted to see the others. I didn't want the dinner to be over. I wanted to find Mort and tell him about this experience. Not in pride but in wonder. And in eternal gratitude.

I was delighted to hear music as I turned left at the doorway. Given God's apparent ease with interior design and moving walls and furniture, who knew what I might find? I was walking back toward the dining room but hoped that I'd find yet another completely new experience. I was getting closer, and the music grew louder. I heard singing. The song was unmistakable: "Imagine."

Those lyrics meant more now than they had at any other time. The DJ certainly had good timing. I wondered if God was behind the turntables. Not too many holy references to God's ability to mix. I cracked myself up thinking about this when I turned left down another hallway. I stopped in my tracks.

Fate stood waiting for me.

"How do you feel?" he asked casually.

"Ironically," I responded without a hint of any, "I feel alive."

"Authentic. Truth. Whole. Peace," he confirmed.

"May I ask you something?" I asked, feeling fearless and changing the subject without thinking.

He nodded.

"What's the real deal with that boy? You're not telling me the whole story."

Fate took a deep breath. "The boy wasn't the only character in that story who went rogue."

"I'm sorry, what's that now?"

"My plan was for the boy to simply crash at the bottom of the hill and have the paramedics come. His mom is single, one of the paramedics is a single dad, and, well, you get the idea. He wasn't supposed to nearly die. The thing is, I didn't factor the car."

Jeezus. What was it with Fate and car accidents?

"You see, it's not all managed, scripted, and predetermined. Like the boy, I didn't see the car coming. I was too wrapped up in my own work to see the bigger picture."

Holy shit! Even Fate misses the forest for the trees? Maybe this is proof that Fate is also just a reflection of myself. Of my energy. I felt so much relief. I felt so much compassion for him. Instinctively, I gave him a hug and tried to joke. "I get it, man. That'll teach you to text and change the universe." I wanted to know what happened next. "So the boy went back and . . . what happened?"

"Out of my hands," he was quick to offer. "It's up to the mom and the paramedic."

I was starting to better understand how it worked. Fate didn't always change the course of our lives; he simply tried to give a nudge from time to time. Fate didn't create the love when two people felt magically connected; they did that. He just provided the opportunity. Even then, it didn't always work out as he envisioned.

As we continued to stand in the hallway, I told Fate that I remembered reading a story about two sisters from South Korea. They were separated as young children. Forty years later, they found each other, now both nurses, working in the United States . . . and in the same hospital.[12]

"That stuff doesn't just happen," I said with a cross between a declaration and a question.

Fate shrugged. "Maybe it does. Maybe it doesn't. We all need some help. Some accept those experiences as God's work or even my own. Some call it coincidence. Some don't need to define it at all, and they are simply grateful. And still some? Some don't even find magic in those situations. They brush it off without any thought at all."

I was curious. "Do you need the credit?"

"I think it all balances out. The Universe isn't perfect. There are a lot of variables," he told me. "We can only do what we can do. Validation doesn't make anything right or wrong. The need for it is a false idol." And he added with a gentle poke in the ribs, ". . . as you know."

I knew that he was right. I didn't always see what was right in front of me, or I did and pretended it wasn't there. He was just happy when people were genuine. That was Fate's only goal. That was God's only goal. I guess that made it my only goal too.

"People are always searching for a bigger, deeper meaning, regardless of their beliefs, but it's all really simple. The secret of life is authenticity. True, unapologetic authenticity. Living in harmony with the soul." Fate was in the middle of explaining in more detail when I blurted out—

"Iwannagobacktoo."

"You do, do you? You want to go back?" he asked with enough of a tone that made me think it was possible. And in a way, that made me think that he had been waiting for me to ask all along. There was a kind of delight and enthusiasm in his query. Playfulness. As though mentally, he was eagerly rubbing his hands together on the verge of finally getting to try out a new magic trick.

"I guess I do," I told him. But only if I knew for sure that I'd be able to take this experience and insight with me. I wanted the "if-I-only-knew-then" secret sauce. What was the point of the do-over if I didn't have the tools to do it over correctly? I wanted a guarantee that I could, in fact, learn from this experience. I wanted to go back with the experience woven into my DNA and also my memory. I didn't want to write another near-death experience book; I wanted to write the first-ever death experience book.

"Can I?" I asked hesitantly, with a hint of anticipation. I joked, "Beam me down, uh, God?" There was just enough of a lag between my question and his answer that I was able to imagine a new life. It was that same kind of "life flashing before my eyes," but instead of flashing my memories just before my death, this slide show was of the experiences I wanted in a new life.

In an instant, I imagined being able to explore and accept an entirely new level of love, not only for myself and Jess, but for all. I imagined the freedom of forgiveness and a conversation with my mom and sister unlike any I'd ever had before. I imagined a future telling my story to packed rooms and inspiring people to achieve what they perceived as unimaginable. I imagined being able to fearlessly speak my mind. I imagined changing lives. Starting with my own. It was such a beautiful picture. I was practically figuring out what to wear for my return flight when Fate interrupted.

"I'm . . . sorry."

"What?" I responded in total disbelief.

"You can't go back, Erik. It's not possible."

"That's it? You're sorry?" I didn't want to accept what he was sorry for. Not immediately. I wanted to hear him say it.

Sometimes, Fate minced words or beat around the bush. Sometimes, he buried the lede. Not this time. I had my life. And for a moment, it felt like I had totally wasted it.

I tried to shake him off without showing much disappointment. "I mean. Sure. Yeah. Right. Duh. Obviously. I was half kidding anyway. I had my time. It's the boy's turn now. Why would I want to go back?"

Fate was compassionate. His voice lowered. Almost to a whisper. Like he wasn't supposed to be telling me this. "You don't really want to go back. It sounds good on paper, but you wouldn't have a memory of what happened here."

I wanted to protest, using those near-death experience books. *They* got to go back! But I didn't protest at all. I didn't say a word. And then . . . the awkward silence.

"Listen. Ummm, I stopped you because I just wanted to tell you that I was proud of what you did with the boy. I wanted to thank you. I'm sorry I raised your expectations for something more."

His words were nice to hear, but my grip on the moment was loosened, and I was still lost somewhere between what might have been and the reality of what was. "Sure. Of course," I mumbled while his "I'm . . . sorry" painfully echoed in my head. The words felt like a concussion. I really wasn't going to hold Jess again. Or make love to her again. I wasn't going to see Timmy or have breakfast with Adam. I knew that now for sure.

"There's more," Fate continued.

"There's more?" I thought I'd had enough.

"Because of what you did, you're now the boy's guardian angel."

"Do I get wings?" I asked sarcastically to hide my discomfort.

"Better than that," he replied.

CHAPTER SEVENTEEN

A struggling young woman is bullied in school. Convinced that her life will never get better, she contemplates harming herself. At a crosswalk, a woman behind the girl sings the chorus to Katy Perry's song "Roar." When the girl finally turns to look, the woman isn't there.

Guardian angel? Do I get wings? Obviously, I was intrigued. What could be better than wings? Wings! I probably could have asked about a hundred questions. In half a second. But I spared Fate as he told me to follow him down the hallway. We quietly walked toward the music. "Imagine" had been replaced by one of my favorite Prince tunes, "Let's Go Crazy." You know the words.

Ironic. Equally appropriate, I guess. Whoever was DJing was inside my head. Had to be God. Right? As we approached the room, I could see arms flailing and bodies jumping. Those with what seemed like professional moves were in lock-step with the White Man's Overbite. Nobody cared how they danced. They only seemed to care that they were, in fact, dancing. "Dance like nobody's watching" was a motivational poster in life. Apparently, a reality in death.

The dance floor was packed with far more people than just those who attended the dinner or even the movie. There must have been another two or three hundred people, but I was never very good at estimating crowd size. I didn't know where they all came from or who they were, but everybody was dancing and singing along to the . . . *wait*. That's no DJ. That's fucking Prince! Prince was playing the after-life party!

Prince was famous for showing up in clubs after his shows and throwing down for another three or four hours. Might as well keep it going in heaven. He might never stop playing here. Prince never struck me as someone to let a little thing like death slow him down. Hell, Prince never really struck me as someone who believed in life, death, or any of it. He lived in some other kind of vortex that we couldn't possibly understand. Artists—the real artists—always amazed me with this kind of spirit. I thought that to believe in your art at such a high level demanded an entirely extra level of belief. You had to allow yourself to detach from the norms of reality . . . and the reality of norms. You had to be above it. Or far, far in front of it with no ability to look back. *Jess was like that.*

I had seen The Purple One in concert a few times. His energy was electric. His performances, inspiring. He would play for two, three, four hours, and what made them even more awesome was that he didn't allow people to use their cell phones to take pictures or videos. No, he wanted his fans in the moment. "*You* bought the tickets," he told us. "Only *you* should get to remember this." It was his effort to give *us* a glimpse beyond the norms. It was a challenge to break the status quo. A dare to experience something in the moment and be unable to share it after the moment had passed. I remember putting my phone in my pocket and feeling relief.

His death sent multiple generations of music fans into a tailspin. We all grieved, but in a strange way, Prince's death made sense to me. He didn't strike me as the kind of artist who should wither away and die. I couldn't imagine an eighty-year-old Prince. I thought his death, like his life, should be a show. Performance art. "God is going to have one hell of a house band," was the party line. Turns out they were right. I was here watching it. Still, I kind of wanted to see God with the headphones behind the turntables. Or maybe crowd surfing. Yeah. God crowd surfing. That would be cool.

I watched as Prince moved effortlessly on the stage. He was reported to have been in significant pain at the time of his death, which is what led to his accidental overdose of painkillers. He didn't seem to be feeling any pain now. Gone was the cane he had used to get around the stage the last time I saw him. The electric moves were back.

There's no shame there—the word people used to describe his death. That was always the party line when an artist died young or in nefarious circumstances. I always hated that. Who were we to say it was a shame? I think our inability to explain our own lives makes it easier to judge others. Duh. Obviously. My God, Prince was beautiful. And back in all his glory.

The room was painted in a purple light. A series of mirrored balls hung from the ceiling and reflected whites and pinks against the purple. Prince invited a group of dancers up on the stage. It was a trademark move. I stood in the back of the room and watched. I liked to watch these kinds of things from a distance. I liked to notice the nuances of things and create stories. I was feeling the love.

"Come on," Fate said. "I want to introduce you to someone."

Really? Now? Dude, that's Prince! Fiiiiiine. I followed Fate through the heavy back doors that completely blocked the sound when they closed behind us. We were standing in a garden. "Follow the path," Fate motioned to his left, where stepping stones led into darkness. "Follow the path," he said again. His tone was one that felt final. Like I wasn't going to see him again. He was passing me on to someone or something else.

I was uncomfortable and defaulted to what I knew best. "This feels kind of like the finale of *The Bachelor,* and you're Chris Harrison. Except he usually says something about your fate awaiting you, but my Fate is right here."

Fate was kind. Fate, really, was always kind. "Follow the path," he repeated. He then turned and walked away.

Fate had given me plenty of paths to follow when I was alive. Most of the time, I didn't take them. Other times, I may have done it without really knowing. I was in no position to walk away at this point. I was in no position to disregard his words. *Follow the path.* I felt like James Earl Jones walking into the cornfield in *Field of Dreams.*

I found myself walking through a garden of light. Streams of color burst from the flowers: reds, yellows, greens, blues, oranges, and more filled the sky and painted themselves across my face and body as I walked. The lights felt warm and soft. They didn't blind me when they crossed over my eyes. I wasn't even thinking about the steps I was taking. When I looked down, I realized why. I wasn't walking at all. I was floating. The lights were lifting me. I felt light in my body and also my mind. This was like one of the stories in those near-death experience books. Where was I going? I didn't know. And it didn't matter. It didn't matter at all. To see all that was around me better, I closed my eyes.

It made perfect sense to me. I finally understood that clarity required surrender. Contentment required surrender. In this moment, I had accomplished just that—total surrender. I always thought that contentment was the goal. I was wrong. It was to surrender. I wasn't on a path. I *was* the path.

Surrender to yourself. Surrender to your soul. Surrender to your being. The rest will happen whether you worry about it or not. Seems so simple now.

I opened my eyes when my feet touched the ground. I was standing on a stone on the edge of a sparkling lake. Crystal-like objects shimmered in the water, and a warm breeze caused ripples to dance across the surface. The lake was surrounded by tall reeds moving with the breeze to create a natural harmony. *Where am I?*

"You're in my backyard," said a familiar voice behind me.

I turned and found a huge grin of crappy teeth. "Ira? What are you doing here, man?"

"Blondie was looking for you," he deadpanned sarcastically. He was good at that sort of thing.

My girl came running through the reeds. As I knelt to pet her, she jumped in my arms and gave me the greatest kisses I had ever received. And just as quickly, she took off running through the reeds. She always liked that—running through tall bushes. It must have felt fun on her fur or something. Anytime she saw tall grass of any kind, she was gone. I watched her with a smile.

"It's beautiful, isn't it?" said Ira.

"I can honestly say I've never seen anything like it. Or even imagined anything like it."

"Totally different from being on those rocks in Joshua Tree, huh?"

Oh, my. I felt my knees get weak. I felt faint. I felt short of breath. I felt . . . I felt . . . "Ira? God?"

He just flashed me that big smile.

That grin that told me he knew more than I did. About anything. About everything. He was just Ira, so I just blurted out, "What the fuck, dude? What are you doing to me?"

He explained, "I can be anything you want me to be. I am your experiences, after all. Right now, you need me to be Ira."

"Yeah, but when I was alive and knew Ira, was that you?"

"Maybe," he said with that Ira grin that was nothing but trouble. "Everyone you meet, every experience you have, and every emotion you feel has some level of God in it, regardless of what you believe or don't believe."

We both stood overlooking the lake. I watched the crystals jump and the ripples dance. I watched Blondie splash in delight. I felt the warm breeze kiss my face. I felt safe. The perfection of the moment was so breathtaking that I think I nearly forgot to breathe.

Ira said, "Follow me."

I didn't give it a second thought as we started walking across the lake. Yeah, I was walking on water. Of course I was. Why not? I had, after all, just floated through a garden, and Ira was God. So why shouldn't I just walk on water? At this point, it felt perfectly natural and normal. For what felt like effect, Blondie swam just in front of me and behind Ira. It made perfect sense to think of Ira as God.

We walked out into the middle of the lake, where a kind of lounge was set up. Two six-foot sofas faced each other on either side of a magnificently carved coffee table. Flanking the sofas and where someone might normally place potted plants or a ficus tree, reeds reached out of the water. If this were a room, art would have been hanging on the walls. Because we were in the middle of a lake, outside, the sky was the art. Shades of pinks, oranges, and reds framed our resting lounges as though we were about to sit in the middle of fire.

Ira said, "Please, sit."

After hundreds and maybe thousands of $250 hours spent sitting on furniture just like this, I felt as though I was about to have one hell of a therapy session in the strangest living room I had ever seen.

Jokingly, I asked, "Is it okay if I lie down?"

"Whatever makes you most comfortable," he said without a hint of a joke.

Oh. I guess I *am* about to have one hell of a therapy session. I stretched out on the couch, instinctively closed my eyes, and took a deep breath. In through the nose. Out through the mouth. Just like all my meditation teachers had taught me. When I opened my eyes, Ira was gone. Sitting directly across from me was the wizard. "Where did Ira go?" I asked, sitting up.

"Just relax," God said. "Nothing has changed. You see me as you want to see me. I'm in your image. People get that part confused all the time."

I closed my eyes again. When I opened them, Blondie was sitting on the couch.

"See what I mean?" she said.

Closed and opened my eyes.

Prince.

Again. My sweet, ninety-six-year-old nana.

Again. Jond.

Again. My high school English teacher who died on the golf course.

Again.

Again.

Again. Even my mom briefly.

It was like *Ghostbusters*. I was afraid the Stay Puft Marshmallow Man might soon be sitting on the couch. Finally, I closed my eyes tightly. And when I opened them, the wizard was back.

"I'm whatever people need me to be," he explained. "For some, I'm just wind. In fact, I think you wrote that once."

He was right. I had written a poem once. I never finished it. I started it when I was in an incredibly dark space, but when I came through it, I couldn't figure out how it was supposed to end:

I prayed to the only
God I know
the one with the voice
that sounds just like
shimmering leaves
when the wind
gently blows

It rambled on after that, but I never figured out what happened when I opened my eyes and stopped praying. It sat on my phone, unfinished, for months. Maybe years. I can't remember. He was right. I could wrap my mind around God as nature. God as the breadth of my experiences. The advice I had received. I heard God's voice in the wind. But my image of God was the stuff of fiction.

As I looked at God now, I just sat with a sense of acceptance.

"Before I ask you the question I have for you, do you have any questions for me?"

Do I have any questions for God? Is he kidding? Where would I start? What should I ask first? I spent my entire life asking questions. I spent my entire life torturing myself with questions. I had spent my time in . . . wherever this was . . . trying to *stop* asking all the questions. I wasn't in the mood to fight myself with all the questions. Still, I was sitting with God, wasn't I? I felt like I had a responsibility to anyone who had ever prayed for such a moment. I hoped I was up to the task.

"Anything?"

"Yep. Have at it!"

God was sitting across from me and had given me permission to ask anything. I could ask him about the meaning of life. I could ask if he felt pain—physical or otherwise. Did *he* have a higher power? I could ask about why humans were so horrible to one another or if it bothered him that humans killed each other in his name. That must cause him pain. I could ask him about the Bible. *Come on, my dude, fact or fiction?* I could ask . . . anything.

Ooooh, I could ask if he *did* have favorite teams and fuck with the outcome. I nearly did. I could ask any of those questions that haunted me. Those questions that kept me up. Those questions that my demons taunted me with. Fucking anything. And I was blank. Well, not blank as much as I didn't know where to start. As I racked my brain to figure out what I should ask, I stopped and thought about what he had just said. *Wait. There is a question for me?* I looked up, and I swear he smirked.

"Can I defer my question until you ask me yours?"

"Sure," he said, "mine is easy." And without missing a beat, "Why did you do it?"

Oh, fuck.

CHAPTER EiGHTEEN

Following a bad divorce and three years of digging herself out of debt, a woman's friends take her to a casino to celebrate her new life. She wins $400,000 on the first pull of a $1.00 slot machine.

I forgot that I had killed myself.

Myriad thoughts tumbled through my head. Wouldn't God know exactly why I did it? Why the need to ask? Is this why I was invited to dinner? I wondered for a moment if everyone at dinner was asked the same question, but I quickly realized that wasn't the case. All these thoughts came one after another after another without God and me ever breaking eye contact. Of course, he knew exactly what I was thinking. No point trying to deflect at this point.

I took a deep breath and started to ramble.

"Truthfully, I think the sequence of events started at birth." I wanted to make a joke, but I wasn't kidding.

God knew I wasn't kidding, but he raised his eyebrows in a way that suggested he best get settled in. He repositioned himself on his couch, nestled in across from me, kitty-corner. Lying on the couch with my hands folded on my chest, I gazed into the rich, colorful canvas of the sky with a completely clear and focused mind. I didn't have to think. I had practiced this story over and over for therapists, friends, and others. Most of the time, in this exact same position. Like an athlete who had perfected his craft, I was reciting a story from muscle memory. This was my ten thousand hours. I'd told this story ten thousand times to a hundred different therapists. Fooled them all.

"I've talked so much about fitting in versus belonging," I asserted. "From a very, very young age, I felt like something set me apart. I knew that I didn't fit in. The fact is, I didn't feel like I belonged anywhere. Like I was a total outcast. That's how I felt my entire life. On my own. Alone. As long as I can remember, I was lost in my own mind. I had thoughts of what I should be. I had thoughts of what I could achieve. I had thoughts of . . . " My voice trailed off. I hadn't even realized that I had started crying, and a lone tear interrupted my stream of consciousness when I tasted the salt. It surprised me.

"I'm babbling." I tried to downplay my grief. This usually worked. But not here. This therapist wasn't having that.

"Keep going."

What choice did I have? "Time and time again, I would generate a certain amount of momentum and stop. I would discover some talent, and I would ignore it. I would take steps toward some—I'll just say it—*destiny*, and then I'd sabotage it. Whether it was a business idea, a creative endeavor, staying in shape, or in a relationship, I'd let the voices in my head and the voices in my life stop me from becoming . . ." I thought I'd continue that sentence, but that was really it. I'd stop myself from becoming. Period. I'd stop myself from being. Period.

A friend once wrote a post on Facebook. It read: "I have spent a lifetime thinking the result of what has come of my life should be significant, but what I think 'significant' should be is what I put into life without fearing or measuring the result. If people want to measure how much money I have made, how far I have swum, or how fast I have run, they can, but I'm certain it will never reflect the person I am. I have never made enough money, have only swum so far, and have never gone fast enough, but when I acknowledge everything that I've put into those efforts, I am certain it *has* been significant, and for all of it, I am grateful."

Such beautiful words. And spot on. That was me. Except I never came to grips with the significance. My friend found the "becoming." I never did. He found belonging. I never did. Instead, I kept trying to be pieces of other people. Because I thought that was cool. It was cool that my friend, Jeff, was a mountain man and could live in the wilderness. I tried it. I liked it, and I even went backpacking several times with him. I wasn't that guy, even as we'd taunt each other with a chant of "I'm a Goddamn Mountain Man!" I'd change my hair. I'd change my style. I'd even change my personality.

In fact, what I was, what I really was . . . was an artist. I was a writer. I was an observer. I saw the world differently than most. I felt the world differently than most. But I never knew what to do with it. I didn't know how to manifest it. I was afraid to record it. I didn't belong and felt like I had to fit in. How could I take something that felt so far outside the box and make it fit neatly into one? I couldn't. And I beat myself up for it.

I saw therapists. I killed relationships. As another friend wrote about himself: "I was not perfect. Not a perfect friend, or brother, or father, or lover, or writer, or son, or . . . anything. I learned through bitter experience that I was going to be weak at the wrong moments, make mistakes and hurt someone I loved, and be arrogant when someone needed compassion . . . I was going to fall short."

I had fallen short too. But that friend also went on to write that he had figured it out. He accepted this about himself. I never did. I just took those moments of weakness and learned to use them against myself. Every single time I took a turn that wasn't in line with my soul, those mistakes, those pains I caused, became whips. I'd sentence myself to hundreds of lashes. The scars that remained were so thick I no longer recognized myself. Or felt myself.

I took another deep breath. "How long do we have?" I asked. Blondie was now sitting on the couch with God. "Come here, girl," I said, patting the spot next to me. She looked at God. He gave her a slight nod as if to say, "Go." She bounced over to me and curled up at my feet. I was grateful the couch was big enough to fit the both of us.

"Sorry, how long do we have?"

"As long as it takes. As long as it takes you to answer the question." It kind of felt like God was challenging me. And for a flash, I wondered what Mort was doing. I tried to bring Ira back. I closed my eyes, and when I opened them, I was surprised to find the guy who introduced me to Ira. The one with whom I had a falling out.

"Why doesn't that work anymore?" I asked.

"Because you don't really want Ira to be sitting here. Your soul isn't in it. You're pretending that's what you want, but it's not really what you want." Then, after delicately tracing the outline of my heart with this verbal knife, he pushed it all the way in. "I know you understand that. That's why I'm here. I represent all of that."

Ouch. The dude didn't mess around. But he was right. I understood. My life was mostly just that.

I zoned out. In retrospect, it's kind of amazing to think that even in that situation, I couldn't concentrate, but I was lost in a dream. Or maybe it was a nightmare.

God was talking to me; his voice sounded like a drone or gibberish. I was wandering through my life. Through an overgrown forest of shoulds and supposed-tos. I was torturing myself with the vivid, not-so-instant replay of my lefts that should have been rights. The stops that should have been starts.

There I was, throwing the summer school catalog at my parents and telling them to pick the classes I should take because they wouldn't pay for the screenwriting and acting classes I wanted to enroll in. What would have happened if I had learned to write screenplays when I was nineteen?

Fast-forward to the job offer I had received to be part of an exciting new event when I was twenty-six. Four years into a growing career, my parents suggested that quitting on the spot to go live in a room with four, five, or ten other guys to do entry-level work and make $200 a week might not be the best decision. I passed on the inaugural event that went on to rival the Olympics. What would have happened if I had gotten in my car that day to drive to Rhode Island to become the assistant to the Executive Producer? Would I have learned to produce TV, which was another dream? Add it to the story.

What about the business plan I wrote when I was living on my friend's couch in Arizona? I was standing at an ATM, reading the ads while waiting for my money, when it dawned on me that securing the advertising rights to high-traffic areas could create a financial windfall. Or at least an opportunity. And, because I was in Arizona . . . golf carts! My roommate and I developed a prototype and even secured the rights to some courses. Then, an angel investor offered us $30,000, and I freaked out. What did I know about starting a business? Better to run away in fear. What if I hadn't? CartAds became another pull on the crack pipe that was my ever-building story.

What about the relationships that I stayed in for too long or the ones that I didn't have the balls to pursue?

The fact is that all these experiences were part of my life, but they all pointed to one fundamental truth: I had never followed my soul. Worse, I had sabotaged it. My entire life was one big game of hide-and-seek. I sought my soul, even as I hid from it. It wasn't hiding from me. It was always there in plain sight.

I once listened to a podcast hosted by a famous author who said readers would send in long emails asking her to help them find their purpose. "More often than not," she said, "it was all there in the readers' words. They weren't looking for direction at all. They were looking for validation."

Those people were also playing hide-and-seek. We wanted the same thing . . . for someone else to make it easy for us. I wanted, no, I *needed* my parents' permission—even when I was well beyond the age where that should have mattered. And when they didn't give it to me, when they didn't validate a job choice, a relationship, or even a car purchase, I'd run from it and blame them when my life went sideways. But it didn't work that way. I just couldn't accept that maybe, just maybe, I had something to offer this world. Or that world. The world. Whatever. Didn't matter. I had never learned to accept it. I had never learned to just tell everyone around me to fuck off. I'd be going left even though they *all* wanted me to go right. I had never learned to trust myself and believe in myself. I wasn't trained that way. *Why?*

Now I was dead because I created so much pain for myself that I couldn't figure out how to stop it any other way. I thought it was my only way out of jail. Maybe that's part of heaven. Figuring it all out. Then again, gaining total consciousness when you're dead sort of feels like hell.

"Erik, are you even listening to me? God to Erik, come in, Erik."

I opened my eyes. "Yes, sorry. What was the question?"

God now showed up in the form of my fifth-grade teacher, Mrs. Brown, my favorite childhood teacher. I always made a point of visiting her at her home long after I was out of elementary school. Here she was, wearing her colorful sweater, slacks, oversized glasses, and with a pencil tucked behind her ear, shaking her head. "You were telling me about—"

I interrupted. "Right."

The colors had changed. The reds, pinks, and oranges had been replaced by greens, yellows, and blues. A hint of purple. When did that happen? I missed it. Blondie was distracted by something in the reeds, and she leapt off the couch, which startled me as much as the tear had earlier. God remained in her same spot. I sat up and put my feet on the coffee table. "Is this okay?" I asked. She nodded.

"I started to seek help from sources I felt were more aligned with who I was. Intuitives. Spiritual guides. People who might be able to help me find my way. Help me discover my soul's true path. I was told, more than once, that I was destined to change the world. I was a level-ten old soul. I was meant to move people. Change lives. It was amazing to hear. This was how I felt. This is what I always knew. Yet, I still didn't know what to do with all this encouragement. It felt arrogant to discuss it. Who would believe me anyway? How could I possibly explain this to my friends? Occasionally, when I would try, I'd be met with laughter. Just like when I was in Boy Scouts. It all just made me feel like more of a fraud. I had dug a deep, deep hole, and the only way out felt impossible.

"So I just kept it close to me and wondered how I would become the person I was apparently meant to be. No, that's not it—how could I be the person I already was? How could I just accept it and honor it by following my instincts? Then I met Jess. She didn't want me to be anything more or less than I was. She accepted every bit of me—good, bad, and ugly. With her was the only place I felt whole."

I thought for a minute about how, really, Jess didn't *make* me feel whole. She just *allowed* me to feel that way. I started rushing through the story for fear of boring God. I mean, she knew all of this, right? She was these things. It felt like she was making me work my way through it all as a kind of penance. At least, that's how I justified the story. I must have told her my entire life story before getting around to my birthday. The day I died. Blondie was back by now and dreaming on the couch. Her little dog feet were jerking around as though she were sprinting. As if heaven wasn't awesome enough for her, she still dreamt great dreams of playing with her friends.

"My last birthday was the most perfect day I had ever experienced. For the first time, I lived according to the answer I had always given to the question of 'What's your perfect day?' I started out with a long trail run. Jess and I made love. I went to my secret writer's hideaway and worked on my book, and though I was initially paralyzed by the words, I started to write. I mean, I *really* started to write. I felt like a writer. I *was* a fucking writer. Then Jess and I met for a picnic and a hike. And on the hike, we made love again. We went to dinner with friends, and then, well, when we got home—we, ummm, we, uhhh—" I stopped.

God was kind. "I know."

"As Jess slept, I walked out onto the back deck to gaze at the moon. It was full and perfect. It seemed big and close enough to touch. I was moved by its presence. I closed my eyes and prayed. I thanked, well, I thanked *you* for an amazing day. A day that I had long dreamed of but had never lived. A day filled with friends, creativity, passion, and love. Deep, deep love. Being with Jess was like nothing else. It was easy. Without a care. Without pretense. I started to follow the moon.

"I walked off my deck and down the trail that leads across the creek to the street behind The Gym. My plan was to walk up the trail on the other side of The Gym and get as close to the moon as I could. I had long talked about climbing up the local mountain at midnight but never had. This day seemed like the perfect day to do it. Because it was a perfect day."

I stopped here. I needed to compose myself. I had been talking for what seemed like hours. I needed to get some water. God told me I could simply scoop up the water on which we were sitting. Of course I could. I cupped my hands and filled them with water. Once. Twice. Three times. The most cleansing water I think I'd ever had. Like after running a marathon. Only this marathon was my life. I splashed some of the water on my face. It was time to answer the question.

"So why did I do it? As I was walking to the trailhead, I thought, just for a second, that I had done it. I had lived my perfect day. I had accomplished something that I never thought I would. I was elated. I sent Jess the text telling her that I loved her . . ."

My voice trailed off.

"And?" God said.

"And I stepped in front of the car."

"But why? *Why* did you do it?"

"BECAUSE I DIDN'T THINK I DESERVED IT! Okay?" Then slowly, in a sad whisper, "Because I didn't think I deserved it." *Sounds so stupid now. But that's why.* I couldn't repeat it. I couldn't live up to it. I felt so selfish and was filled with so much shame for even wanting it. Every voice in my head told me I wasn't enough and I was never going to be. The feeling was so overwhelming that I broke the one rule I ever made for myself: "If I lose this battle, I do it alone. Nobody else can be involved."

I broke that rule when I included the driver of the car. He never saw me.

God sat still. Silent. I was tremendously uncomfortable and nervously shifted on the couch. *Please, say something. Anything.* I wanted to crawl under the couch and hide. If my definition of God was truly the sum of my experiences, including the people I knew, loved, and respected, well, I now felt like I was letting them all down.

"I know it was a big mistake," I said, finally. "It's something I must live with—or whatever, you know what I mean—for the rest of eternity, I guess. Every time one of my friends dies and comes here, I'll have to tell them the truth." *My God. How will I tell Jess? How will I tell her that I didn't think I was good enough even after my perfect day?*

When someone died from suicide, if anyone left behind snickered about selfishness, I was always the first to put an end to it. "We have no idea the kind of pain that person must have been feeling. We have no idea about the battle raging in that person's head," I'd say. I could imagine it because I felt it.

For decades, I managed to win the daily battle of staying alive. That's what each day was. A battle for life. Sometimes, the battles were easy, but sometimes, they were excruciating in a way that few would understand. None of my friends really knew. I had won so many battles. Thousands upon thousands. Almost all of them. I had a nearly perfect record. But this is the kind of game that losing just once—even if you've won a million or a billion times previously—is all that matters. The one loss is all that matters.

God tried to settle me. "What would you do differently?"

I started rambling. "Honestly, I don't know. I've come to realize that maybe peace isn't what I needed to be searching for. I needed to surrender first. Surrender and accept. If you're asking how I would change things . . . I'm not entirely sure I'd be able to. I'd certainly want to be more open to accepting myself. I'd want to stop the chase to be something more or different than I was. Stop feeling like I was only valuable if someone else said I was."

I took a deep breath. "But I can't say for sure what that would do. I was always better at helping others than helping myself. I don't regret that part. Not for a second. I suppose, if anything, I'm sorry I didn't do more of that. I just didn't know what that meant. I still don't think I understand what the words of those intuitives mean. They don't matter, anyway. I still don't really know what I would do."

I laughed as I said, "Long story short, I guess I'd like to think I would be more accepting of myself. I'd write. I'd create. All in. Whatever came after that . . . I have no idea. I just now realized how the importance of being an artist or a creative person actually held me back. What would I do? No labels. No fitting in. No belonging. I'd be all of me. And I'd love myself for it."

God sat in more silence. She was good at this. She stared at me. I met her gaze as best as I could but had to look away from time to time. Was she thinking? Was she even here anymore? I don't think she was blinking, and given that she was more or less just a spirit and not really that body—maybe she had taken flight? I waved my hand in front of her face like you do to someone who is daydreaming. I stopped short of saying, "Earth to God." She just stared straight ahead.

Finally, she took a long, deep breath that felt like she was on the edge of frustration. "You haven't figured it out yet, have you?"

"Figured out what yet?"

"You. This place. Where you are. What you're doing here."

"Well, I sort of thought I just finished painstakingly detailing how I killed myself." I tried to laugh a little to make a joke of it. It wasn't funny. "I sort of thought I was in heaven."

And then another bomb. "You're not."

CHAPTER NiNETEEN

*An elderly man saves a drowning eight-year-old boy in China.
It was discovered that thirty years earlier, the same man saved
the boy's father from drowning.*[13]

Oh, fuck. What the hell? This isn't heaven? Where the hell am I? Was this a dream? A nightmare? Was I going to wake up in a cold sweat on some street corner? How long had I been asleep? Metaphorically, I know I'd been asleep for pretty much my whole life save a few moments here and there, but literally, I mean.

God cleared her throat to pull my attention back, then proceeded to challenge me. "Erik, think about all that you just told me. Think about the life you lived. Think about your experiences. I can't tell you. You need to see it for yourself."

I didn't understand. I had *no* idea what she was talking about. I felt anxious. I wanted to throw up. I felt stupid. Blondie, of course, was having none of it and remained in her bliss. Whatever God was talking about, she was in on it. I felt lost. I stared at God. She just stared back. What was I missing? *What the fuck am I missing?*

"Can I have a hint?" I finally cracked.

"Nope." Mrs. Brown was enjoying my pain a little too much.

I closed my eyes, took a deep breath, and tried to replay what I had experienced. There had to be a clue somewhere. What was I missing? The first thing I saw was God's house, or whoever the hell's house it

161

was. Blondie and I were coming up on it, and, *oh wow, that's weird;* I remember the beautiful driveway lined with roses, but I totally missed the line-up of tricked-out golf carts in what looked like a valet area. They were the super cool ones that my dad and his friends drove around in Palm Desert. Were they there before, or did I make them up because I was just talking about CartAds? Doesn't matter. This whole thing can't be about golf carts.

There's Ira. There's me running through the house as I figure out . . . *a billiards room?* Where did that come from? That wasn't in the house back when it was being sold, and I certainly don't remember it when Blondie and I were getting the grand tour from Ira. I was going to open a pool hall once. Funny, with the same college roommate. Billiards was blowing up as the go-to bar game, and game rooms were popping up everywhere. We secured an awesome space, but city codes shut us down. The laws hadn't caught up with the trends, and the college town in which we lived prohibited bars from having more than two pool tables. Fucking idiotic. Just another dream that died.

My eyes instantly opened wide. There was Ira. Smiling knowingly. My heart was leaping through my chest in the same way it did when I was on that rock in Joshua Tree a million years ago. I didn't know how to ask. I felt silly for even having the thoughts.

"Yes?" God teased.

"This whole thing has been a setup!"

"Explain what you mean."

"I'm not . . . this isn't . . . I mean, it's not . . ." I was stammering to find the words. I knew exactly what I wanted to say, but I just didn't know how to say it. Finally, "This isn't my heaven. It's my dead dreams? This has been one long look at all the dreams I let die. CartAds, the pool hall, but—"

"Look closer."

Holy shit. Willie, the young baseball player, was just the manifestation of my very first dream—to play professional baseball. I was going to play for the California Angels or Los Angeles Dodgers. I was going to be the greatest outfielder who ever lived.

And Ira. I saw him because he was a symbol of all the projects I let die. Not just the web series with him, but all of them. The books, the movie scripts, the acting. I think he represented anything, everything creative. Rosa, the old Italian lady who helped me inside, was the dream I had for my relationship with my mom, or really my entire family.

Mort. Mort was the romance I dreamed about. The love at first sight. The family. The unbreakable bond I wanted. I dreamed of it. Even if I didn't think I deserved it. Every person represented something I had given up on. Every single person at the dinner table. They represented dead dreams of travel, of going back to school, of being a wise, spiritual mentor. They represented dead dreams of, well, all of it. Jond? The dead dreams of my childhood. The boy in the hat? That was the ultimate dead dream. The dream of me for myself. Becoming and being me.

Perhaps, I finally got it. Fate's charge wasn't to make God laugh by putting random people together. Fate's charge was to help people make their soul path come true. They simply had to accept the invitation. I shook my head and laughed a little under my breath.

"Is this what purgatory is?" I asked. "People talk about it as some kind of unknown dark place, but is it really about coming to grips with your lies? Only then do we get to see what heaven really is?" It made sense to me. Before, I couldn't understand why there were still so many damn questions in heaven. It's because I wasn't there yet.

"You're still missing one really important point," God offered.

"Are you going to sit there in silence and make me suffer until I figure it out?"

God sighed, smiled, and then explained the missing piece. "This entire experience," he said, "is yours and only yours."

He went on to explain that nobody has the same life. Nobody sees things exactly the same way. Even people who worship the same God experience it differently. Our entire existence is created in our own hearts and minds. It's our canvas to paint. We lose track of just how much we have within our control. But only if we can learn to control our thoughts. Only if we can believe. In ourselves. In something. In anything. That's exactly where I tripped over and over and over again.

Nobody ever has the same experience in heaven. Some may never reconcile their dead dreams. It may not be that important.

"For you, though, Erik," he concluded, "it is paramount."

He was right, of course. I carried so much regret from letting ideas like CartAds or the billiards hall slip away. I beat myself up for decades over projects I never finished. I created narratives like, "I'm an ideas guy, not a follow-through guy." Such thoughts are just self-fulfilling prophecies. That's all these narratives really are. They're insidious beasts that fool us into thinking that they are protecting us from some future failure. Instead, they are jailers that keep us locked up. I needed to make peace with the regret. I needed to change the story in my head.

I asked Ira why it felt so scary to let go of old stories.

"Mostly because you'll lose people."

I didn't understand and suspect my furrowed brow and cocked head gave me away.

He continued. "In repeating these stories, you have taught people what to think of you and how to treat you. If you no longer accept the limitations you place on yourself and your dreams, some of the people you think are your friends won't like it. They will fight to keep you small."

"Why?" I asked.

"Because they are scared too."

Wow. This made sense to me. It explained why I got so excited when I would finally try to express myself in what felt like more authentic ways. Or when I would try to start a new project. Only to become incredibly defensive and angry when one person shot it down. That's all it took. One. "Yeah. It's a stupid idea." That's how it usually went. And I'd slink away in shame. The shame of not honoring my inner voice. The shame of more regret. Shame then became more lies and more bad decisions.

Damn, why was it so fucking hard to express myself? To express my needs?

Why must it be *courageous* to write or sing or speak publicly?

Why did I play so small and put others on a pedestal for no real reason?

Why did I think someone was better than me or that I didn't deserve their time?

I thought I knew the answer to these questions. All that therapy had to be good for something. But why couldn't I get beyond it? Despite knowing I was capable of so much more, of living so much bigger. I know we have life experiences that get trapped inside of us and create these damn narratives. We are born perfect and immediately begin getting reprogrammed. *Fuck.*

God interrupted my thoughts. "At some point, you have to trust that you have all the information you need. You need to trust that you have nothing to fear. You need to stop lying to yourself and others."

"Bu. . ." I tried to interrupt.

God wasn't having it and kept talking.

"Enough. These are choices, Erik. At some point, you have to take responsibility for your own life and make your own choices."

"Bu. . ."

This time God just put up his hand.

"The struggle you're having right now is that you think the right choice should feel easy. But choices are often at their most difficult in the moment. Then, they mature into ease. They don't always start that way."

I was feeling scolded, but God was exactly right. I *did* think that the right choices should feel light and flowy. With a heavy sigh, I got lost in my head, considering CartAds, the pool hall, the sports ticket website I didn't pursue, the girl I didn't ask out, and all the other chances I didn't take. All the times I didn't speak up. My mind was spinning with visions of "What if this?" and "What if that?" and. . . *wait!* I suddenly understood that these broken dreams were all exactly the same thing! They were all manifestations of me not trusting myself. They were all opportunities to trust myself and follow through. And I didn't respond to the invitation. For a second, I wondered if Fate had anything to do with any of them. *Well, if he won't trust himself with that* one, *maybe* this *one will take.*

Trust myself.

Trust myself.

Trust myself.

Was this the reconciliation? I wasn't sure. It felt like it. God and I sat in silence. I took a deep breath, closed my eyes, and said a prayer of gratitude. When I opened them, Ira was gone.

CHAPTER TWENTY

Challenges at home result in a woman losing her job due to poor performance. She tells the story to another woman in the elevator who notices the family picture in the box she's carrying. The other woman offers her a new job before they reach the lobby.

My former camp director and I now sat together, watching the colors shift. I had screwed him over when I was just out of college. I had committed to working for him as a unit head, but three days before the summer session was about to start, I took another job and left him hanging. The other offer was more of a career than just "working at camp." It was a decision that changed my life forever. I didn't understand camp could also be a career. This decision was one of the great "sliding door" moments of my life and one I thought about often. I felt whole at camp, but I didn't let myself have it. I didn't trust myself. He forgave me instantly. It made sense that he was God at this moment.

We watched Blondie splash in the water. This moment sort of felt like those times when a sports announcer lets a dramatic event play out without any words. Like a walk-off home run in the World Series. Only, instead of listening to the deafening roar of a crowd, I was lost in the sounds of birds singing along to breezes strumming tall lakeside reeds.

My eyes were closed when God said quietly, "I'm just thinking. What would happen . . . Nah, never mind."

"Are you serious? No. No. No. God does not do that." I was practically jumping out of my skin. For starters, I practically invented that. And furthermore, no. God, of all . . . of all . . . of *all* . . . whatever he is, does not hesitate to share his thoughts. "Spill it."

More fucking silence. *This guy is killing me with the silence.*

"You have an idea? What is it?" I fidgeted some more. No amount of time spent learning to meditate and listening to Andy on the Headspace app could prepare me for this. That said, I did love Andy's voice. Had a bit of a man crush on that guy. But now, he was no help to me whatsoever. My mind was spinning.

I had thought about dying nearly every day of my life. Like I told God—the story started from birth. But to finally talk about it so openly felt like a relief. I kind of wanted to spill the beans on all of my deepest, darkest secrets. On all the other dead dreams that were probably lurking around somewhere. Even all the mistakes and transgressions. Every lie. Every cheat. All of it.

Andre Agassi wrote a book called *Open* in which he eviscerated himself. I imagined him running a sharp blade from his throat to his belly and opening his rib cage, exposing his heart, offering his soul, and saying, "Fuck it." I knew it couldn't have been easy, but I also knew he must have felt amazing when he was finished with it. I had wanted to do the same thing as soon as I finished reading it. To write something transformative, and just cut myself open. If I could just unleash my soul and free the skeletons, my desire to die would also be released. I can't be judged if I accept open responsibility for all of it. Nobody can. Accountability is the ultimate salve.

Headspace Andy would be annoyed with me right now. I was off in la-la land and nowhere near the moment. It was a defense mechanism that I had refined for decades, but it was also the genesis of a pattern. I brought myself back from Andre Agassi and his remarkable journey to follow his soul's truth.

I asked, "So you said something about an idea?"

"I'm just trying to find the right words."

I was slightly comforted by the fact that God could struggle for the right words. Then again, this God is my manifestation. So maybe it shouldn't be surprising at all. I kind of liked the idea of a flawed God. He caught me in that thought.

"I don't know about 'flawed,' but I understand what you're thinking," he said.

I had managed to impress plenty of therapists with my basic knowledge of myself. Say a couple of profound things, and you're off the hook. Those therapists couldn't read my mind, and I could get away with it. No doing that here.

"Come on, man," I said. "Out with it."

"Fine." He took a deep breath, which caused Blondie to cock her head in anticipation. "You wanna go back?"

Frozen. I was frozen. Like when I was frozen on the field after our game. I tried to talk but couldn't make a sound. I was trapped inside my body. Finally, I said carefully, "But Fate said I couldn't go back."

"I know. And I certainly appreciate that. Think about that for a minute. Which one of us do you think would have that kind of ability?" He had a whimsical look as he mimed a scale with his hands and said, "God. Fate. God. Fate."

I smiled. "Are you throwing Fate under the bus right now?"

"Not at all. There are just certain things that the boss has to do. Fate did exactly what he was supposed to do when you asked about going back. It's his job to let you or anyone else know that they can't go back. You don't think you're the first person to ask, do you? You're not *that* special."

I think that was a joke. I hoped that was punctuation for the sake of levity.

"I didn't mean to imply that—"

He cut me off. "Relax. I was kidding."

"So. Um. What do you mean, do I want to go back? You mean *go back*, go back? Go back to where? To when? What will I remember? Back to Jess? Back to Timmy? I don't understand!" I was completely losing my shit. "Do I just wake up in front of The Gym? Before or after the car hit me?" *Does the car even hit me? Maybe I didn't break my only rule after all.*

God held up his hand.

I stopped talking immediately.

"Breathe." He held his arm up like a yoga instructor. "Inhale through the nose. Exhale through the mouth."

We did this together a few more times. My heart rate returned to normal.

"The thing is," he continued, "I kind of need you to do something for me."

"Sounds a little *Godfather*-esque. You need me to take someone out?" The joke fell flat.

"I need you to write about it."

"Write about what? This? Dinner? My life? You? What?"

He continued. "This whole place is kind of a big secret. It is exactly why most near-death stories are kind of vague and similar. We make sure they go back with white lights and magic. I'm not discounting those stories in any way. They're very real. They happened. Some people just aren't ready for this place, and we send them back. We've never sent anyone back, however, who *was* ready to be here."

There was no way to count the number of times I thought about checking out. I didn't necessarily pray for it to happen. Okay, yes, I did. I thought it would make things easier. In my mind's eye, there was no fitting in or belonging in heaven. There was just being. Acceptance was the law of the land. Surrender was inevitable because there weren't really any other options. So when I had blurted out to Fate, "Iwannagoback," it was in the moment. Now that the reality had sunk in and I was certain it wasn't going to happen—I wasn't so sure.

"You can take some time to think about it," God assured me.

"How much time? Like an hour? A week? A decade? Forever?"

"Time doesn't really work that way here."

I thought he was going to say "down here." For a split second, I wondered if earth was hell. From here—everything was pretty much "down." Based on my experiences so far, maybe anything not here was hell. Maybe "hell" was just a catch-all brand like TiVo. Maybe it wasn't a place at all, but instead, just a state of mind. We often say, "I'm in hell," to describe horrible situations. Maybe "hell" is just being caught in a state of perpetual horribleness. No need for fire and brimstone. Satan is not necessary. Or . . . here comes another maybe . . . maybe Satan is kind of like God and is whatever we decide it is. If that were true, I certainly wouldn't have any problem imagining what Satan would look like. Sort of like when I was on the couch opening and closing my eyes to see God as Blondie, Nana, or Ira. Satan would look like an old boss, that one ex-girlfriend, and maybe the friend who ghosted me when I needed him most.

Funny thing is, it might be easier for me to imagine Satan than God. I think I lived more comfortably in darkness. I was certainly more creative. The best stuff I wrote came from my imaginary Satan more than it did from my imaginary God. At least, I always thought it was my best stuff. Maybe I was just kidding myself. Maybe it was just another old narrative that kept me locked up. *Stay dark. You create better here.* Seems ridiculous. Art should heal, not imprison. All those people I blamed that I imagined as Satan: my mom, my sister, my dad, colleagues, clients, you name it. *Pathetic.* But now I knew that the only person who really put me through any kind of real hell, the only person who deserved to sit in Satan's seat . . . was me.

"Wow, you really torture yourself, don't you?" God took me out of yet another mind spin.

"Everyone deserves to be good at something."

"Listen, Erik, it didn't have to be so hard. It never did," God said, and as I started to interrupt, he held up his hand again. "You did most of that to yourself. You *knew* exactly who you were at a young age. You *knew* exactly what you wanted to do."

"Yeah, but—"

"Exactly. 'Yeah, but.' 'Yeah, but.' 'Yeah, but.' I'm sorry to be so blunt, but your life got lost in all those 'yeah, buts.' These broken dreams you've come to grips with were killed by 'yeah, buts.' *You* did the work.

You had moments when you were able to get out of your own way, but for the most part—you remained your own biggest roadblock. You decided that you needed permission from everyone for everything. Nobody forced that on you. It's cliché to say you were your own worst enemy, but you were. Seems maybe you still are. Forgive yourself. So you can finally trust yourself."

Forgive myself. There it was again. Just like Mort said.

I had enough therapy to know why I behaved in certain ways or made certain decisions. I was armed with reasons. Reasons can go one of two ways. Reasons properly cared for, encouraged, and manicured become beautiful gardens of personal growth. Unattended, mismanaged, and not properly watered, however, reasons become excuses. They become blame. Demons feast on blame. They die from growth. Growth is demon-poison. My reasons became overgrown forests of excuses. My demons thrived. I think I decided the only way to finally kill the forest was to kill myself. It got *that* bad.

Suddenly, God said, "I didn't intend to lie, but I think I may have."

"Wait. I can't go back?"

"Oh, you can still go back, but you don't have as much time as you need. Giving you more time just makes it worse. This proposal wasn't meant to cause you more angst. It was meant as a gift."

"Ask me again."

"Erik, would you like to go back?" And before I could answer, he continued. "You may or may not remember any of this. You hoped that the boy would just 'have a feeling.' Well, that may very well be what you experience. Or, and this is important, you may go back with nothing changed. So would you like to go back?"

I took a deep breath, gave Blondie a kiss on her head, and said, "See you someday, old girl."

God smiled.

"Yes," I told him. "I would like to go back. It's hard to say that I regret what I did, considering this experience, but I do. And I don't want to regret anything. Not anymore. I want to see what it feels like to be . . . to be . . . to be . . . myself."

Ever the entertainer, God tried to be funny. "Take a moment, say your goodbyes."

"Really? Are you kidding?"

God just shrugged as Jond, Mort, Ira, and the others were now walking out to the lake. My heart was jumping through my chest. I wondered if *they* would remember that I had been here. Would they be able to watch me and check in on my progress? Other than the bit at dinner, though, I hadn't really seen any evidence that those in heaven, or wherever this was, could see what was happening on earth. Maybe it was something that came with acceptance and surrender. It's a reward, of sorts, for having the kind of total peace in your heart that comes from making total peace with yourself. That kind of made sense to me.

The only times I ever cried as hard were in times of sadness. Out of feeling lost. I was neither. As tears streamed down my face, as I said my goodbyes and see-you-laters, I was smiling hugely.

Afterward, I found Fate and gave him the last hug. "I figured you out, you old clown. Thank you."

It was time to say goodbye to God. If there were words for a time like this, I didn't know what they were. So . . . I said nothing. I let the moment speak for itself. I looked God in the eyes. I saw myself for a quick second. The silence said more than I ever could. And then I thought of the question I wanted to ask.

"Wait. How do I write about it if I don't remember anything?" And then, "Does everything really happen for a reason—"

Before I could finish, I was gone. I knew the answer anyway. Just like that. The last thing I remember was God mouthing, "Trust yourself." And rolling his eyes at me.

CHAPTER TWENTY-ONE

*A man finds the name "Esther" written in pencil on a dollar bill.
As he has just started dating a woman named Esther, he decides to
frame it and give it to her as a gift. Several months earlier, after
a breakup, Esther had written her name on several dollar bills.
She told herself that she would marry the man that brought her
one of these dollars. They later marry.*[14]

That was fucking close! Standing at the start of the trailhead and basking in the bright light and quiet warmth of the full moon, I felt grateful that the SUV speeding past The Gym had just missed me. I hadn't even noticed the car as I walked with my head in my phone, texting Jess. It was a black Mercedes. They were always black. Had I not stumbled, causing me to look up for a split second before I walked into the intersection, I'd be dead.

I gave myself shit for being the idiot dressed in black and wished the driver luck. *Hope you make it safely to wherever you're going.*

I made it to the hidden dirt patch masking the beauty of what lay just beyond the rusty fence and started to climb. This was my trail. I knew every nuance. I knew the dip a hundred yards up on the left and the tree just beyond with the broken branch that hung out over the creek. It was about 1,500 feet uphill from the trailhead to the spot below the peak. One of my happiest places.

Even though I knew this climb as well as I knew the long drive down Interstate 5 from San Francisco to LA or the curve in the back of Jess's spine, the top of the mountain was always further than I thought. And just like arriving anywhere after a long drive, or arriving at the base of that curve . . . I was always grateful for the journey. Especially arriving at the base of that supple curve.

This was a completely different experience. Having never done this hike at night, I hadn't considered that the smells would be different from those during the day. The sounds of happy singing birds were replaced by howling coyotes and crunching footsteps in the darkness. I spun around on multiple occasions, squinting my eyes. *What's out there?* Darkness always has a way of making you feel like you're being followed. The happy daylight shade of a tree painted by the sun becomes menacing shadows when chiseled by the moon.

One of my friends had asked me multiple times to join him on a full-moon trek. "A silent quest," he called it. There would be no talking. No flashlights. The moon would be our light. With one excuse or another, I always declined. The idea freaked me out. *What if I got lost on the mountain? Not getting any sleep would totally mess up my schedule.* I was intimidated by the depth of my friend's soulfulness. As I hiked alone, I started thinking that my excuses were valid. The truth was, I felt embarrassed by the thought of not being able to keep up. Or of having him see how nervous I was. Old stories die hard.

I wasn't sure what it was about this night that inspired me to "go climb a mountain," to borrow the line printed on the front of my favorite T-shirt from Yosemite I wore as a kid. All I knew was that I couldn't sleep. It wasn't like the usual "couldn't sleep" where my mind was racing with a million different anxious thoughts. Those tortured nights when I replayed all the pain I had caused or wondered why I kept wasting my days.

No. I was calm. Awake. Peaceful. So I took a walk. And ended up on my trail. Perhaps it was a reaction to the perfect day. I had, for the first time ever, lived a full day exactly as I wanted. Every moment. It was a great birthday, and perhaps I just didn't want it to end.

I walked past the small, heart-shaped rock that marked the halfway point. I first noticed it six or seven months ago while walking the trail in a particularly dark space. No bigger than a silver dollar, the rock was a perfectly shaped heart. My instinct was to pick it up, like finding a lucky penny, put it in my pocket, and display it somewhere in my house. Or maybe give it to Jess. I wondered how long it had been there. I unconsciously channeled those feelings I had so many years before in Joshua Tree when I lost my footing and kicked the rocks from their place.

The first time I saw this rock, it reminded me that I had love in my life, even as I was feeling deeply sad and filled with shame. So instead of picking it up, I sat with it. I looked at it. It was perfect in every way. *How does something like this just happen? Isn't it fascinating?* I wondered to myself. When we need something, we often find it. But we must be open to noticing. Since first seeing the rock, every time I walked past this spot, I expected it to be gone. The fact that it was still there showed me that maybe even a rock can have a bigger purpose. How many people had seen it? How many had missed it? How many were as affected by it as I was?

A couple of therapists had pointed out that I was on some spectrum. I was never surprised by this, of course. I had lived with myself since birth. I had lived through *all* of the highs and lows. *All* of the mood swings. *All* of the mania. But damn, the highs were magical. They were all so full of hope. Full of plans. Full of possibility. I felt this way as I continued my walk up my mountain. My senses were heightened, and even the fear I would normally feel as unidentified steps crunched leaves in the woods around me was at bay. I tried to walk the trail with my eyes closed. I made it a few steps before stumbling on a root. Luke Skywalker, I was not.

The creeks were running, and I could hear the waterfall calling me. Letting me know that I was nearing my destination. During years of drought, the waterfall was mute, and I missed our conversations. I was pleased it welcomed me back with rushing excitement. *Hello, old friend.* I had arrived.

Time had already marked the end of my birthday, but the moon was one last candle. I couldn't blow it out, but I closed my eyes and made a wish on it anyway. A wish for Jess. My lovely Jess. As I made my wish, I wondered if she knew that I was gone. I had been careful not to wake her. Not that I could. She slept like a hibernating bear—the result of being the most aware and spiritually centered person in history. She went to bed in complete harmony with her life. She knew and surrendered to her place in the universe and its place in her, which, if you ever spent time with her, made it seem like she was gliding when she moved.

I knew that in the rare event that she had woken up to find me gone, it wouldn't make a difference. She wouldn't worry. Not because she didn't care, just the opposite. She cared so much that she accepted I sometimes "just had to do something." Usually, this meant taking a long drive down the coast. For a while, it was on a motorcycle. I had a beautiful Harley I would ride for hundreds of miles and days at a time. I'd pull off roads, roll out the pad, sleep for a few hours, and carry on. Riding my motorcycle was the most peaceful time of my life. Those nights under the stars were the nights I felt closest to God. Whatever that meant.

Just after high school was the first time I drove to Morro Bay, parked at the beach, and fell asleep in the back of my SUV while listening to the rhythmic patterns of the crashing waves. My favorite sound until I discovered crunching aspen leaves. Few things could ever make me feel more at ease than the crashing surf at night. So different from the way it sounded during the day. It was like the waves were talking to me. *Everything will be okay, Erik. Just relax, Erik. Somewhere, something or someone has your back, Erik.* And sometimes, *Dude, would you just fucking breathe?!* Even the waves could get frustrated with me.

Sitting just off the trail, listening to the waterfall, and leaning back against my favorite tree, I closed my eyes to imagine the sounds of the surf. I imagined riding my motorcycle to the beach. I imagined making love to Jess under the stars. I was startled when I heard crunching leaves. I wasn't alone.

I slowly opened my eyes to find a deer standing nearby. Not unusual on the mountain. After all, I was more on her turf than she was on mine. Yet, something about this deer was different. The fact that she seemed completely unmoved by my existence was a little weird. She wasn't scared. She stared at me. She was small. Like a pet.

"Are you okay?" I asked. "Where's your family?" In my experience, deer typically traveled in threes, and a buck couldn't be far off. It tilted its head like a dog. Like Blondie. Even though she had been gone for forty years, my childhood dog, Blondie, was always easy to access in my thoughts. She used to cock her head just like that. I'd never seen a deer do it, though.

The deer kept staring at me when it started to paw at the dirt. Blondie used to do that when she really wanted to play. It was her challenge to me to find a ball, a stick—anything. She would play fetch for hours. Anytime. Anywhere. If I didn't go find the ball or stick, she would. She had a sixth sense for tennis balls. I never had to bring one with us on a walk because I knew she'd find one. We'd be walking, and she would dive into the nearby ivy and come out with a ball as though she were a cat hunting gophers. I was tempted to throw a stick and see if the deer would chase it.

The most special thing Blondie and I had was a kind of secret handshake. My sister thought I was crazy when I told her that Blondie and I would communicate with each other. I couldn't believe those memories were flooding back. I couldn't believe the deer reminded me of her so much.

Suddenly, the deer walked right up to me and pressed her forehead against mine. That was exactly what Blondie would do. That was exactly our secret . . . I could barely breathe.

Oh, my God.

It all came racing back to me.

Blondie.

God.

Mort.

Jond.

Ira.

The boy.

Fate.

Prince!

All of it. I remembered everything. I was a guardian angel! I . . .
Shit.

I *did* step in front of the Mercedes.

Didn't I?

I was here on this mountain. I could hear the waterfall. I could see
the glimmering lights of the city in the distance. I realized that while
I may have done it, I wasn't dead. I was here. On top of this mountain,
showering in moonlight. Very much alive. For maybe the first time.
Ever. I took a deep breath and gave the deer a long, gentle pat on the
head. *Thank you, Blondie.*

Had I been given a second chance unlike any other? I felt like I
was completely open and aware but also wearing a kind of transparent,
impenetrable armor. I was completely exposed yet unable to be harmed.
Total vulnerability was the best defense against any attacks from demons.
Instead of running from fear, I could move toward it. So easy. If I
welcomed my demons with open arms, they'd have no idea what to do.

I needed to get down the mountain. I needed to get to Jess. I needed
to try to understand what any of this meant.

What do I do now? It was a question, but it wasn't the same kind of
question. It wasn't one of doubt. It was one of anticipation. Excitement.

As I hustled back down the trail, I felt an overwhelming urge to
text Timmy. It was the middle of the night or the very start of the
morning, but I didn't really care. Besides, there was every chance
that he was awake and on his way home from somewhere or saying
goodbye to someone. He certainly wouldn't understand this story—
ever the scientist, ever the atheist—but he'd understand the text: "I
love you, man."

I sent that same text to Adam, Dan, Scotty, Steve, Andrew, Sandy,
Andy, Jeff, the Pauls, and all of the people who had, knowingly and
unknowingly, propped me up as I continued to fall down.

"Things are going to be very different," I said out loud to myself. And, maybe as an assurance to God that he hadn't made a mistake . . . even if God was just me. Which, therefore, meant I *was* just saying that to myself. If I tried to figure it out, I'd make my ears bleed. So I laughed at the absurdity of it all. Because it was absurd.

How will I ever write this book? People were going to think I was crazy. People were going to write reviews telling me I was a terrible writer or just flat-out stupid. "Yes, they are," I again said out loud. "And that has nothing to do with you."

It was around 4:30 a.m. when I got back to the house and quietly climbed into bed. I kissed Jess on the top of her head and pulled the covers over me.

It wasn't more than a couple of hours later when my phone started blowing up. The texts were all the same: "Are you okay?" *Better than ever,* I thought. I'd respond in a bit.

Jess was still asleep. I wanted so badly to wake her and share this story, but it was more important that I started writing. I had my assignment. Whether it came from God or from somewhere inside me, it didn't matter. I quietly gathered my backpack, threw on my jeans, pulled on my boots, and . . . damn, the café didn't open until 7:00 a.m.

I had approximately forty-seven minutes to kill. I decided to drive to Mo's, park, and walk the path that lined the bay.

As I walked, I began recounting the story in my head. I started to imagine the feedback and fallout:

What the fuck are you talking about?

How could any of this be true?

You didn't die.

You didn't meet God.

You weren't sent back to earth.

What is wrong with you?

You fell asleep on a mountain and had a weird dream.

You got high and wandered out of the house and hallucinated this entire thing.

It's a fantasy.

You might not have been on the mountain at all.

It was all a dream.

You fell asleep after sex.

That is all fake bullshit.

Plus, you're a shitty writer.

"All of this could be true," I told myself. I laughed when I thought that the last bit about being a shitty writer would likely use "your" instead of "you're." And then said loudly, "Who gives a fuck?"

I had spent my life worrying about what other people would think. Doing things for others first. Asking for permission. But I had a story to write. We all have something inside of us, yearning to break out. The thing that is uniquely ours. I had spent too many years suppressing it, which only served to cause great injury to my soul. I was writing for me. And then I *really* understood. I was writing for the little boy who ran away from home. I was writing to forgive myself. I was writing to trust myself. Writing *was* trusting myself.

As I watched a lone, standup paddle boarder work his way across the glassy bay, I realized something else. I needed to call my mom.

CHAPTER TWENTY-TWO

A couple strolling on a beach finds a message in a bottle. The message is the wedding vows of a couple that had recently gotten married across the big lake. It turns out the couple that found the bottle had gotten married on the same day years earlier.[15]

I sunk deeply into my mom's living room sofa. The same one from my childhood. The cushions, which had never been replaced, were impossible to get up from if you were over thirty. My mom sat across from me in the oversized chair with the blue floral pattern. People often say, "You could feel the tension"—well, in this case, I could also hear it and taste it. It sounded like the piercing scream of a child and tasted like metal.

Then I just started . . .

"I'm sorry."

My mom started to cry. This was not easy for me. Ever since the fight, I was trained to avoid hurting women. I knew her tears were more relief than pain, but tears were tears. A single tear was kryptonite. This waterfall of tears derailed me from my plan.

I wanted to tell her the whole story. I wanted to tell her that I had tried to kill myself by stepping in front of a car. Or that I *had* killed myself. I wanted to tell her that I saw her at my funeral and was sad to realize that we no longer knew each other. I wanted to tell her that I saw the conversation she had with my sister, and I had hung out with Blondie. I wanted to tell her I met God. I wanted to tell her about Joshua Tree and all the dreams I gave up on. Instead, I just said I was sorry.

She said she was sorry too. As she started to tell her side of the story, I felt my entire body tighten. I was trying to get as small as I could. My arms crossed. My legs crossed. Molded into the couch. I was trying to disappear. I felt hot. My heart raced. I was thinking of all the places I'd rather be at that exact moment. I didn't like it. Her words. The way she spoke. Slowly. Deliberately. As though I was one of the first graders she once taught. It made me crazy. I felt so much . . . so much . . . so much . . . shame.

Shame!

"Stop! Stop! Stop! Please, stop talking!" I suppose it must have felt rude from where she was sitting, but I had to tell her how I was feeling.

I told her that love had been hijacked by shame.

"Oh, my God, Mom . . . this has nothing to do with you."

Through the tears, I told her that I felt shame. When I was seven, she and my dad had those fights, and especially when she hurt herself, I abandoned myself. I promised that I would try to take care of her. I promised that no woman would ever feel pain. My dreams would come last. I wouldn't make choices without permission. This became my life. I didn't know what an inner child was then. I didn't know what trauma was. But it all made sense now.

This wasn't about her at all. *Idiot. It was always about your relationship with yourself.* It finally made sense. I was fighting myself. I needed to forgive myself. *Just like God said.* Forgive yourself. Forgive yourself. Forgive yourself.

I finally understood why I picked the relationships I did. I finally understood the lifetimes of sabotage. Of yo-yo weight gain and loss. I finally understood why I wanted to die. Every day. I finally understood. And I tried my best to explain it.

She was listening. She was crying. I was crying. Decades of old, dark wounds were being exposed to the light. Light heals. The subjects of hundreds of hours of conversations with therapists were finally being discussed. I told her that I surrendered. I surrendered the past. I surrendered to the reality of the moment. To the present. "We are both doing the best we can. We need to trust that."

I told her that I forgave myself.

I forgave myself.

I forgave myself.

I forgave myself.

She spoke. Quietly. "When your grandmother was eighty or so, I sat on her bed and asked her why we didn't get along. We both wanted to. We just forgot how to talk to each other." She then said, "I don't want to wait until I'm eighty for us to figure that out."

Then I just blurted it out. "Mom, I tried to kill myself."

I told her everything.

By the time I got to the part about God sending me back, we were both sitting on the couch, sinking into those quicksand pillows. I tried to break the tension. "I don't know how you're going to get off of this thing." We laughed. For the first time in a long, long time.

"I didn't know how to talk to you," she said.

"I know. I see it now. I was unconsciously ashamed of my life, and I blamed you. You never had a chance when we talked."

"I got scared. You were so callous and short with me. I felt such anxiety whenever I picked up the phone. I felt like everything I would say was wrong."

"I know, Mom. And I'm sorry."

The wounds were healing with each word. My wounds. Her wounds. I told her about my friend who told me that I had to get things right or I would regret it forever.

"I have enough regrets, Mom," I said. "I don't want more."

We had to get this right.

And then she asked me why I liked watching cars.

"I didn't realize you knew about that!"

"I'm your mother, Erik."

Yes. Yes, she was.

CHAPTER TWENTY-THREE

*A writer who started a book twenty-five years ago tells his son that
he's not going to work on it any longer. Too much time has passed,
he explains. The book is going in the drawer and will never be
considered again. That same day, the writer gets an email from
a publisher who wants to help get the book out.*

Jess and I were settled into a faded, faux leather booth in the straight-out-of-central-casting midwestern diner. The server wasn't quite sure what to do when Jess ordered a veggie burger, so she brought her a small dinner salad. "Closest thing we've got, honey." On the other hand, I figured *when in Rome* and ordered what they called "The Specialty Burger" and fries. The sign on the table proclaimed that it was *All about the sauce!*

When it arrived, I wasn't sure what made it so special. It seemed to be your standard burger with all the usual stuff, but that first bite . . . *Holy shit.* It was amazing. I did not know what was in the sauce, but I was ready to bottle it and start a new business. And the fries were perfect. The few that I had anyway. Jess might not eat any red meat, but the woman could mow fries with the best of 'em!

We were seated against a window, wolfing down our food and gazing out onto the perfectly Mayberry-esque street. It was an early Saturday afternoon, and the locals were out and about. Kids wearing their baseball uniforms, families on bikes, dogs walking themselves. A banner stretched above the street proudly announcing the upcoming chili cook-off to be held the following weekend at the nearby park. It was a living screenplay, and we were extras on a small-town movie set.

"I would love to be here for that," I told Jess. "I bet that's some of the best chili ever."

"It is, honey." Our server was back with our check. "Take your time, honey." Everyone was "honey."

The family of four in the booth next to us was clearly celebrating. Two parents and their kids, a couple of brothers who were probably nine and thirteen, were laughing and making toasts.

"To the Cubs!" said the younger boy in his Little League uniform. The older kid put his arm around his brother and said, "Great job today, Stevie. That was a bomb!"

His dad was athletic-looking and beamed with pride. I assumed he had played his share of baseball in his day, and seeing his kid hit a home run must have made him feel pretty good.

There was a time when I wondered if I had missed out by not having any kids. Would I be celebrating my kids' athletic achievements? Would I have been able to teach them about perspective, compassion, and belonging? I liked to think that I would have been a good dad, but . . . I stopped myself. I learned to understand that it just wasn't meant to be. I had other responsibilities that precluded such opportunities, and I had dedicated myself to them. Plus, after some time, I had discovered how fun it was to spoil the shit out of my nephews and nieces. Jess knew what I was thinking. Jess always knew what I was thinking. She just took my hand and smiled at me.

I couldn't help but chime in. "Hey, man, go yard today?"

Stevie replied, "Yeah! First one! I crushed it!"

Stevie's mom gently reminded him of the importance of staying humble and not to brag.

"I get it, man! That's a huge accomplishment!" I reassured them both that I took no offense. "I never hit one. I played for ten years when I was a kid and never hit one. I don't think I ever came close! When you're in the Major Leagues, I can tell all my friends that I saw you the day you hit your first home run!" I asked Stevie for his autograph.

Jess and I got up and walked to the register. I handed the server $200 cash for our meal and told her that we'd also like to pay for Stevie's family. I quickly wrote a note on the receipt, "Good job, Stevie! Keep that ball forever!"

"But combined, the two tables are only $83.27," the server told me.

"I know."

We walked out before she could object or even say thank you. We smiled and waved as we walked by the window and saw the server bringing Stevie an ice cream sundae. She was talking to the parents, who looked perplexed and then, with wide eyes, waved back. I gave them a thumbs-up and then mimed swinging a bat. I don't think too many people from out of town ever came to this place. Most visitors were probably family or had a personal connection to this place. So, a couple of random strangers handing out money must have seemed totally foreign.

The next day, I was speaking at a university fifty-something miles away. Reading from my novel about fortune cookies. It was the first book I wrote after my experience because I wasn't ready to write this one. Whenever I did these events, we always randomly found small towns to check out. This wasn't the first time. It certainly wouldn't be the last. This town, though, was a little further away than the ones we typically picked. This town was special.

We continued strolling down the small street and came to an intersection. Four-way stop sign. I waited. I watched as car after car waved on the pedestrians. Not once did a car try to cut in front of anyone. They all stopped. They all waved. It was beautiful. This dance was a waltz. Not a mosh-pit.

I asked a little boy in a Cardinals uniform if he could tell us where the field was.

"Just go straight down this street for two more blocks. It's on your right. Can't miss it, sir."

Sir. Small towns. I chuckled.

We walked our two blocks, and the field appeared exactly where the young Cardinal said it would. Norman Rockwell couldn't have painted this more perfectly. We had apparently walked into the 1950s. There was a single field. A small fence lined with banners honoring the sponsors arched around the outfield. The local plumber, insurance agent, barber, and café all supported their local Little League. A small 200-foot sign was dead center, and similar 180-foot signs were in left and right field. Not surprisingly, it was impeccably manicured. The American flag danced in the wind above center field. We got there just as the game was about to start.

I smiled at Jess as we settled into the bleachers behind home plate. I took her hand in mine.

The umpire, a teenager, maybe fifteen years old, wearing jeans, a white T-shirt, and a backward red hat, walked toward the plate. The logo on the faded hat was from a Minor League team. Probably not far from here. I watched him closely as he greeted the coaches in the home team dugout. Small town, they knew each other. He scanned the crowd stands as though he were searching for someone. He waved at a woman I assumed was his mom, who sat beside a man in a paramedic uniform. Then he got to me. We locked eyes. And he stopped dead in his tracks.

I smiled and gave a gentle wave.

He smiled cautiously and waved back. Maybe he knew.

Maybe he just had a feeling.

THE END

EPILOGUE

After reading this manuscript, Jess told me she liked it and then added, "Kind of a Disney ending, isn't it?" I knew what she meant.

I'd love to tell you that I'm healed. How everything is perfect. I'd love to tell you that I have it all figured out now. That everything is great with Jess all the time. That my relationship with my mom is smooth and easy. That my sister and I talk every day.

Those would be lies.

My work continues. My work will always continue.

I *have* learned to trust myself. To forgive myself. And to love myself. Mostly. Mostly is far better than rarely. And infinitely better than never. I'll take mostly.

The truth is, I had decided to quit writing this book. It was too hard. I finally gave up and made peace with the fact that it would remain unfinished forever. I tried. But even though I had written my fortune cookie book, which had some moderate success, I couldn't find a publisher interested in this one.

On the same day I locked *Dinner at God's House* in a drawer for what I thought would be forever, I received a note from a publisher accepting the manuscript.

I'm still nervous about it. I still struggle with imposter syndrome—like all artists do, I suspect—but I am a writer. The only way I know how to be a writer is by sending this book out into the wild. After that?

Dunno. That's not my responsibility. I did my part. I trusted myself to say what I needed to say.

Maybe the rest is up to Fate.

ACKNOWLEDGMENTS

My friend, Jacob Nordby, famously wrote, "Blessed are the weird people: poets, misfits, writers, mystics, painters, troubadours, for they teach us to see the world through different eyes." These are exactly the characters I need to thank. After twenty-five years of writing this book and more than fifty in total, I've collected quite a few of them.

First, I thank my family. Because, as you might imagine, being part of this creative journey required a certain amount of patience. Being part of the entire journey, though? Let's just say it can be a lot.

To Lisa and Kolby, the true artists in the house, I'm grateful for your support, understanding, forgiveness, and *forgiveness*. For a very long time, I didn't have a temper so much as a specific tone that was devastating. I didn't use it a lot, but when I did—it was mostly at home. I hope it's gone forever. You never quit on me. I'm lucky to keep learning from you and look forward to seeing what you create. Also of note—many thanks to Haley. The amount of healing that comes from unconditional love, hours of walks, and playing fetch can never be understated. (With love and belly scratches to Harley, Guinness, Mutsy, and Roi. I hope you've all found each other.)

To my mom, dad, and brother: sharing this manuscript with you has been one of the most important and difficult acts of my life. My story is not your story, and while this book looks through a fictional lens, it's also not-so-fictional. I know it was hard to read. But you did. I'm proud of the relationships we have been courageous enough to explore and reimagine. It might have been easier not to have the hard conversations, but we did and do, and we're all better for it, I think. I know I am. Thank you. Thank you. Thank you.

Now to all of you misfits, heretics, artists, and mystics: You are represented in my life by names like Tim, Susie, Mandi, Dick, Krista, Rachel, Marvin, Elizabeth, and Adam. I cannot name all of you, and I hope you'll forgive such trespass. I hope I have told you enough privately how deeply grateful I am for your presence in my life. Without you, I'm not here. You are friends, family, teachers, and loves. Therapists. So many therapists. Some have been around for decades, and others for a blink. Some remain and some, as they do, have slipped through the fingers of time. In this book, I define God as the sum of the experiences of my life. I believe that. As a result, it means each and every one of you, no matter the experience, is God. You're part of me. That's no small thing. Moreover, it means that every new experience we share makes God grow. I'm grateful for that.

Lisa Rojany, Lisa Fugard, Lauren Sapala, Anna-Marie O'Brien, Beth Howard, and Jacob Nordby, you all read this book throughout the years. You shaped it, challenged it, and willed it into existence. You wouldn't let the story die even when I wanted it to. Even when I wanted to. Your souls are in these pages. Your hearts, in mine.

To the group of men I've collected as confidantes and sages, guides, and yes, jesters—including a strangely large number of Pauls, a Dan, an Andrew, a Rob, a Steve, an Andy, a Sandy, a Kareem, and others— thank you. Your words, wisdom, truths, and perfectly timed, loving silences pulled me from the depths time and time and time again. I trust you know who you are because I'm confident I've told you how much I love you time and time and time again.

Mondo Cozmo, Rick Rubin, Joy Oladokun, WRDSMTH, and Jason Isbell, thank you for being tiny pinpricks of light when there was only dark. For being a single ray of warmth when I was shivering in the cold. For inspiration in times of desperation. I suspect it's a complicated burden to know your art saves lives. It feels like an impossible responsibility to be true to your craft and still accept its power. Maybe I'll be lucky enough to feel that someday.

Dan Harris, your book *10% Happier* was a launching pad. Your work helped me better understand meditation and all those asshole voices in my head. I suspect I've gifted your book more than any other. I reference it in these pages. Maybe you will read this one. That would be cool.

Finally, to the team at Wellness Writers Press: Julie Colvin, Leila Summers, Rebecca Bruckenstein, Lynn Thompson, as well as the hundreds of people who donated to bring this book to life: Thank you. I cannot believe that *Dinner at God's House* is being freed after twenty-five years. It's overwhelming.

There's so much more to say. So many more to thank. Maybe that's for the next book.

Much love.

NOTES

Chapter 2

1 Spain, Sarah. "Runs in the Family." *ESPN*, September 2, 2018. www.espn.com/espn/feature/story/_/id/24505521.

Chapter 3

2 Mullin, Gemma. "Newly married couple find old picture of themselves playing on the same beach as children just a few feet apart...11 years before they met and fell in love." *Daily Mail*, July 31, 2014. www.dailymail.co.uk/news/article-2711816.

Chapter 6

3 Crockett, Zachary. "Two Girls, a Golden Balloon, and Fate." *Princeonomics*, July 11, 2014. www.priceonomics.com/two-girls-a-golden-balloon-and-fate/.

Chapter 7

4 Woolcott, Alexander. "Reunion in Paris." *The New Yorker*, July 22, 1932. www.newyorker.com/magazine/1932/07/30/reunion-in-paris

Chapter 8

5 Littlechild, Chris. "The Uncanny Case Of The Jim Twins, Two Estranged Twins Who Led Identical Lives." *Ripley's*, May 28, 2018. www.ripleys.com/weird-news/jim-twins/.

Chapter 11

6   Bernath, Brianna. "'Just you wait': Man keeps promise to marry preschool sweetheart, 20 years later." *Today*, June 30, 2017. www.today.com/news/20-years-later-these-preschool-sweethearts-got-married-t113358.

Chapter 12

7   Castle, Angelina. "The lost wallet, a great love story!" *Steemit*, 2017. steemit.com/story/@angelinacastle/27-the-lost-wallet-a-great-love-story-60-days-motivational-stories-series.
8   Robinson, Phil Alden, dir. *Field of Dreams*. Gordon Company, 1989, DVD.

Chapter 13

9   Watts, Alan, W. *The Culture of Counter-Culture: Edited Transcripts*. Boston: Tuttle Pub, 1999.

Chapter 14

10   O'Kane, Caitlin. "Nurse reunited with NICU baby she cared for 28 years ago – he's now a resident at the same hospital." *CBS News*, September 4, 2018. www.cbsnews.com/news/nurse-reunited-with-patient-she-cared-for-as-a-baby-28-years-ago-resident-lucile-packard-childrens-hospital-stanford/.

Chapter 15

11   Weinrib, Adam. "Vin Scully's list of Hank Aaron facts proves Braves had guardian angel." *Dodgers Way*, November 21, 2021. dodgersway.com/2021/11/07/dodgers-vin-scully-hank-aaron-braves-tribute/.

Chapter 16

12   "Sisters separated 40 years ago in Korea reunited working in same US hospital." *The Guardian*, October 11, 2015. www.theguardian.com/world/2015/oct/12/sisters-separated-40-years-ago-in-korea-reunited-working-in-same-us-hospital.

Chapter 19

13   Zhao, Christina. "Man Pulls Drowning Boy From River, 30 Years After Saving the Youngster's Father." *Newsweek*, August 10, 2018. www.newsweek.com/man-pulls-drowning-boy-river-30-years-after-saving-youngsters-father-1067814.

Chapter 21

14   Gray, Lauren. "40 Amazing Coincidences You Won't Believe Actually Happened." *Best Life*, June 14, 2019. bestlifeonline.com/weird-coincidence/.

Chapter 22

15   "Vow in a bottle uncorks a wedding coincidence." *NBC News*, October 1, 2007. www.nbcnews.com/id/wbna21086323.

Made in United States
North Haven, CT
28 June 2024

54169511R00115